FUNNY SKITS AND SKETCHES

BY
TERRY HALLIGAN
DRAWINGS BY JOYCE BEHR

PLAYERS PRESS, Inc.
P.O. Box 1132
Studio City, CA 91614-0132

FUNNY SKITS AND SKETCHES

PLAYERS PRESS, Inc. P.O.Box 1132, Studio City, CA 91614-0132 U.S.A.

Simultaneously Published in:

Australia, Canada, U.K., U.S.A.

Printed in U.S.A.

Halligan. Terry.

Funny skits and sketches / by Terry Halligan ; drawings by Joyce Behr.

p. cm

Includes index.

Summary: A collection of humorous skits and sketches, suitable for auditions, schools, talent shows, and community functions, and primarily linked with specific holidays.

ISBN 0-88734-688-X (alk. paper)

1. Children's plays, American. 2. Young adult drama, American. 3. Schools Exercises and recreations. 4. Holidays Exercises, recitations, etc. [1. Holidays Drama. 2. Humorous plays. 3. Plays. } I. Behr, Joyce, ill. II. Title.

PS3558.A387F8   1999

812'.54--dc21   99-21313

CONTENTS

*This book is dedicated with love to
all the young actors and actresses
from Madeleine School,
Portland, Oregon*

BEFORE YOU BEGIN

Practically everyone loves acting. Pretending to be someone else, putting on costumes and performing for others is a favorite activity for people of all ages. But not everybody has the time, the ambition or the desire to produce a full-length play. Even a one-act generally calls for a huge investment of time and effort.

These skits and sketches don't! They're short, they're silly, they're fun, and they serve a very important purpose. As a teacher, I'm always looking for brief but entertaining plays to use in the classroom, in assemblies, in revues and talent shows. Not everyone can (or wants to) sing or dance, do magic tricks, standup comedy routines or monologues. And what's left for all those others? Skits and sketches, of course!

That's how this book came about. All the plays in it were written to order. Created by me, tested and refined by lots of my students, they fit our needs perfectly.

First, they're funny. At least, we think they are. They appeal to the sense of humor of the kids that read them and see them.

They have lots of action and good parts that are fun to play. Some of them also have interesting parts for those who are a little shy, but want to be in the play too.

They deal with situations that are relevant to youngsters and are resolved in ways that audiences find hilarious.

Also, they're short. Most of them are so short you can read them once and ad lib them immediately. This makes them especially valuable because you don't have to spend hours and hours rehearsing (and it looks as if you did!). You can use as many or as few skits as necessary, depending on your need and the size of your group.

Another thing that makes these skits so useful is that they call for relatively few props or costumes. This makes them easy to put on at a moment's notice. And you can do them anywhere—in the classroom, on a stage, at home, at scouts, in small groups or in clubs. Kids of all ages can perform them (very few of the plays key in to any definite age group).

Besides the skits, the book includes a selection of even shorter plays we call "blackout sketches," that are mostly based on jokes. Blackout sketches move fast and the lights go out suddenly at the end. These sketches are wonderful "quickies" to do in the classroom or between longer skits in a show. They're a little like the vaudeville numbers that used to be performed in front of the curtain while the stage was being set up for the next act. And you can use them in that same way too.

Staging is loose. I've ended each skit with a curtain closing, and each sketch with a blackout. This way, all the skits and sketches will work on a regular stage. But you can also use them in a much less formal setting. If you're in a classroom or at home, just turn the lights out at the end of the skit, or carry a sign across the stage area saying "The End."

Most of the skits are based on the holidays of the school year, because it's so difficult to find appropriate material to perform at these special times. But we've also included a solid collection of skits and sketches you can perform any time to fill out a program.

So—get a group of kids together and choose your skits. Add your own ideas and variations (the first skit in this book, *Twelve Days of Christmas*, was created by a class that had a marvelous time deciding on the "gifts" they could give from their own over-stacked closets!). Use the stage business we've provided or invent your own. Stick in lines that relate directly to your characters and events in the lives of your audience. Be zany and crazy. Crack each other up. Don't be afraid to be a ham. The audience *wants* to laugh. And everyone can have fun with these funny skits and sketches!

Skits &
Sketches
for Winter

TWELVE DAYS OF CHRISTMAS

Characters

NARRATOR
STEVE
TONY

Setting the Stage

This is a take-off on the song. Characters could even sing it if desired. No special costumes are necessary. This skit calls for many props (all listed in the text). STEVE needs a long table on which to place the gifts. You can change the items to suit the things you have, as long as they fit the idea of the sketch. You can also make fake items to look like items listed. This skit is really fun because as it goes along, the audience begins reciting the gifts along with the characters.

SCENE. STEVE's *house.* STEVE *is onstage.* TONY *enters carrying a small knob with a red bow on it.*

NARRATOR. On the first day of Christmas my best friend gave to me a knob for my color TV.

STEVE. What is it?

TONY. A knob for your color TV.

STEVE. Gee, thanks, just what I needed.

(*He shakes his head and puts the knob down in front of him.* TONY *exits.*)

NARRATOR. On the second day of Christmas my best friend gave to me two old gloves.

(TONY *returns and hands* STEVE *two old gloves.*)

STEVE. Thanks. Now I have two old gloves and a knob for my color TV.

TONY. You're welcome.

(*He exits as* STEVE *puts the gloves next to the TV knob.*)

NARRATOR. On the third day of Christmas my best friend gave to me three french fries.

(TONY *enters, carrying three french fries.*)

TONY. There would have been more, but I ate the rest.

STEVE. That's okay. It's the thought that counts. Now I have three french fries, two old gloves and a knob for my color TV.

(TONY *exits and returns with the next gift: four tennis shoes, each one different.*)

NARRATOR. On the fourth day of Christmas my best friend gave to me four tennis shoes.

TONY. Sorry they don't match.

STEVE. They're—uh—interesting. Let's see now— I have four tennis shoes, three french fries, two old gloves and a knob for my color TV.

(*He places them in a row on the table.* TONY *exits and returns with the next gift.*)

NARRATOR. On the fifth day of Christmas my best friend gave to me five insect wings.

TONY. I used to collect them.

STEVE. What are they?

TONY. The wings off bugs.

STEVE. How original. Five insect wings, four tennis shoes, three french fries, two old gloves and a knob for my color TV.

(TONY *exits and re-enters with the next present.*)

NARRATOR. On the sixth day of Christmas my best friend gave to me six paper napkins.

STEVE. Another present? What is it this time?

TONY. Six paper napkins. You never know when you'll need these.

STEVE. Wow. Six paper napkins, five insect wings, four tennis shoes, three french fries, two old gloves and a knob for my color TV.

(TONY *exits and returns with the next gift.*)

NARRATOR. On the seventh day of Christmas my best friend gave to me seven cans of icing.

STEVE (*looking at cans*). Icing?

TONY. Sure! It's really delicious!

(TONY *exits.*)

STEVE. Okay—seven cans of icing, six paper napkins, five insect wings, four tennis shoes, three french fries, two old gloves and a knob for my color TV.

(STEVE *continues setting the gifts on the table as* TONY *brings more.*)

NARRATOR. On the eighth day of Christmas my best friend gave to me eight dirty stockings.

TONY. Sorry, they're kind of dirty.

STEVE. I can wash them, I guess.

(TONY *exits.* STEVE *adds the stockings to the line of gifts and points to each one as he says it.*)

Eight dirty stockings, seven cans of icing, six paper napkins, five insect wings, four tennis shoes, three french fries, two old gloves and a knob for my color TV.

(TONY *returns, carrying a big box of balls.*)

NARRATOR. On the ninth day of Christmas my best friend gave to me nine balls for bouncing.

STEVE (*holding up a couple*). A baseball, a basketball, a tennis ball . . .

TONY. Yes, there are nine, but some of them are a little flat. (*Exits.*)

STEVE (*pointing to items*). Nine balls for bouncing, eight dirty stockings, seven cans of icing, six paper napkins, five insect wings, four tennis shoes, three french fries, two old gloves and a knob for my color TV.

(TONY *re-enters with prayer books.*)

NARRATOR. On the tenth day of Christmas my best friend gave to me ten books for praying.

STEVE. What are these?

TONY. My old prayer books.

STEVE. I can always use these. (TONY *exits.*) Now I have ten books for praying, nine balls for bouncing, eight dirty stockings, seven cans of icing, six paper napkins, five insect wings, four tennis shoes, three french fries, two old gloves and a knob for my color TV.

(TONY *re-enters with records.*)

NARRATOR. On the eleventh day of Christmas my best friend gave to me eleven songs for singing.

STEVE. What now?

TONY. These are some of my old records.

STEVE. Gee, thanks. There's "I'm a Little Teapot," and "Mary Had a Little Lamb" and lots of other favorites. I sure have a lot of stuff now. I've got eleven songs for singing, ten books for praying, nine balls for bouncing, eight dirty stockings, seven cans of icing, six paper napkins, five insect wings, four tennis shoes, three french fries, two old gloves and a knob for my color TV.

TONY. I'll be right back.

STEVE (*without expression*). I can't wait.

TONY. This'll be the last gift.

STEVE. Oh, darn.

(TONY *exits*.)

NARRATOR. On the twelfth day of Christmas my best friend gave to me twelve cards for playing.

(TONY *re-enters with some playing cards.*)

TONY. Sorry I don't have a full deck.

STEVE. You're telling me.

TONY. I've lost some of them.

STEVE. Some? There are only twelve here.

TONY. I know. Maybe you can think up a game to play with them.

STEVE. Now I have twelve cards for playing, eleven songs for singing, ten books for praying, nine balls for bouncing, eight dirty stockings, seven cans of icing, six paper napkins, five insect wings, four tennis shoes, three french fries, two old gloves and a knob for my color TV.

TONY. Well, that's it!

STEVE. Thanks. You're really a great guy.

TONY (*ready to exit, turns and speaks to the audience*). Thank goodness, I finally got my closet cleaned out!

(TONY *exits as the curtain closes.*)

THE END

YOU SHOULDN'T HAVE

Characters
KIM
MICHELE
MOLLIE
KATY

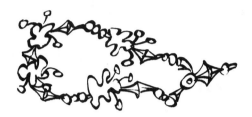

Setting the Stage
No special costumes are necessary. An extremely un-usual necklace is needed—the stranger, the better. A box with Christmas wrap and a bow are also needed for the gift.

SCENE. KIM *is busy putting the finishing touches on her Christmas present for* MICHELE.

KIM. I can't wait until Christmas to give Michele this present. I just know she's going to love it. I think I'll go next door and give it to her right now.

(*She crosses the stage and knocks on* MICHELE*'s door.* MICHELE *answers.*)

MICHELE. Hi, Kim. (*Pointing to the present*) What's that?

KIM. It's your Christmas present. I couldn't wait, so I came over early to give it to you.

MICHELE. Oh, really, Kim, you shouldn't have.

KIM. Go ahead, open it, I can't wait to see the look on your face.

(MICHELE *opens the box and pulls out a very unusual and ugly necklace. She tries to think of what to say.*)

MICHELE. It's—uh—uh—it's really one of a kind! You shouldn't have. (*Turning to the audience*) She really shouldn't have.

KIM. I just knew you'd love it! Well, I've got to go home now—bye!

(*She skips off happily.* MICHELE *looks at the necklace, shakes her head, tries it on and then takes it off.*)

MICHELE. Yech! No offense to Kim, but this really isn't my type of necklace. What am I ever going to do with it? I know! I'll give it to Mollie for Christmas. Maybe she'll like it. I'll just put it right back in this box and take it over to her now.

(*She crosses the stage and knocks at* MOLLIE's *door.* MOLLIE *answers.*)

MOLLIE. Hi, Michele. Who's the Christmas present for?

MICHELE. It's for you. Open it.

MOLLIE. You shouldn't have! (*She takes the present.*) I just love presents! (*She opens it.*) Oh, my, it's—uh—well, it's really lovely.

MICHELE. I'm glad you like it. Well, bye, see you later. (*She leaves happily, speaking to the audience.*) I'm glad I got rid of that!

MOLLIE. What a perfectly awful-looking necklace! What should I do with it? I could give it away, but then Michele might ask where it is. I know! I'll leave it out here in the street and someone is bound to take it. Then I can tell Michele it got stolen.

(*She leaves the present and goes back into her house.* KATY *comes walking by and sees it.*)

KATY. Oh, look, a present. I think I'll open it! (*She does.*) How ugly. I shouldn't leave it here, though. I know! I'll give it to Kim for Christmas. I'll just put it back in the box and take it to her right now.

(*She goes to knock at Kim's door.* KIM *answers.*)

KIM. Hi, Katy. (*She sees the present.*) That's a pretty present. In fact, that looks a lot like some wrapping paper I bought.

KATY. It's for you.

KIM. Oh, Katy, you shouldn't have!

KATY (*to audience*). I know, but I did.

(KIM *opens the present, pulls out the necklace.*)

KIM. Uh—gee, thanks, it's really—uh—nice.

KATY. You're welcome! I'm glad you like it. (*She exits.*)

KIM. That Katy has awful taste. Who would *ever* choose an awful necklace like this?!

(*She throws it into the wastebasket as the curtain closes.*)

THE END

THAT'S MY CHAIR

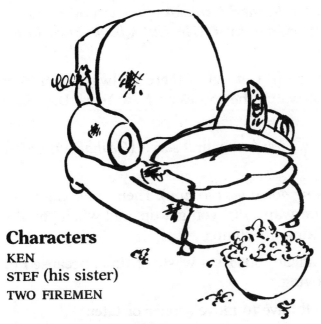

Characters

KEN
STEF (his sister)
TWO FIREMEN

Setting the Stage

STEF and KEN need no special costumes. Each fireman could wear a hat and raincoat and carry an ax made from cardboard. Furniture needed: 2 chairs, a television set and a telephone. Other props: some snacks, a box of old clothes, sports equipment.

SCENE. *Living room.* KEN *enters, turns on the television set and prepares to watch.*

KEN. New Year's Day and I'm going to sit here in this nice comfortable chair and watch the games on television. (*He sits and relaxes.*)

STEF (*enters and looks at* KEN *angrily*). Hey—that's my chair!

KEN (*looks at her and then looks the chair over*). I don't see your name on it. (*He settles back down in the chair.*)

STEF. I mean it! Get out of there. I always sit in that chair to watch the games on New Year's Day. Now move!

KEN. Sorry. First come, first serve. (*He makes no effort to move.*)

STEF (*sitting down next to him*). Then I'm going to sit here and wait until you get up, and when you do, I'm getting *my* chair.

KEN. Go ahead, but it's a waste of time, because I'm not moving.

STEF. You'll have to move sooner or later.

KEN. No, I won't.

STEF. Yes, you will, and when you do, I'm getting that chair!

KEN. Nothing can make me move.

(STEF *exits and returns with a tray of snacks. She sets it down on the floor just out of* KEN's *reach and begins eating.*)

STEF. Oh, this is delicious! You should try it.

KEN (*reaches for the bowl of popcorn, but she pulls it away*). Come on! Give me some, too!

STEF. Sure. Come and get it.

(*She puts it just out of his reach so that he'd have to get up to get it.*)

KEN (*stubbornly*). I'm not moving. You can have your dumb old popcorn.

STEF. Okay, but it's awfully good!

(KEN *looks longingly, but doesn't move. The phone rings.*)

KEN. Answer it. That could be important.

STEF. You answer it.

KEN (*starts to get up, but then remembers*). Oh, no you don't! I'm not answering it.

STEF. Okay, I will. (*She answers the phone.*) Hello? Yes, he lives here. He did? That's wonderful! What kind of contest? He would? Oh, no! I'm sorry, he can't.

KEN. What is it?

STEF (*covers the phone with her hand*). It's some Football Bonanza contest. All you have to do is answer the question and you could win a big prize.

KEN. Really? (*He stands up.* STEF *gets ready to rush to his chair. He sits down again quickly.*) No way. You aren't tricking me into getting out of this chair!

STEF (*on telephone*). Sorry, I guess he doesn't want a big prize. I can? Okay. (*She listens to the question.*)

Sure I do—it's called a touchdown. I do? I win? Oh, thank you! You'll send me *my* prize? That would be great! (*She hangs up and runs back to her chair.*) I won a hundred dollars!

KEN. A hundred dollars? Oh, brother!

STEF. Now will you just give up this ridiculous game and let me sit in my chair?

KEN. No way!

(STEF *leaves. A scream is heard from offstage.*)

STEF (*offstage*): Help! He's going to murder me!

KEN. Stef, are you okay?

(*He starts to jump up out of his chair, but then realizes it's a trick.* STEF *peeks in the doorway to see if he's out of his chair. He runs back to it.*)

STEF. You rat! What if I was really being murdered?

KEN. Then I guess I could sit in my chair all the time, couldn't I?

STEF. I *will* get you out of that chair! You'll see.

KEN. No way.

(STEF *leaves again and returns with a box full of* KEN's *clothes and sports equipment.*)

KEN. What are you doing now?

STEF. I decided this is the perfect time to clean out your closet. I'm getting rid of a few things. I'll just take these old things out to the trash can.

KEN. But that's my new shirt. Those are my good clothes! That's my favorite football. You can't get rid of that stuff!

STEF (*smugly*). Then come get it. (*She puts it outside.*)

KEN (*starts to get up but changes his mind*). It's okay. I can get it all back later. The garbage man doesn't come on holidays.

(*Just then a fireman comes running onstage.*)

FIREMAN. Fire! Fire! I'm afraid you people will have to evacuate the building!

KEN. But we can't!

FIREMAN. You'll have to, for your own safety. You'd better hurry! The fire is spreading quickly!

KEN (*realizes he's telling the truth, jumps up out of his chair and begins running around in circles*). This is real! Oh, no! What shall I save?

(*He frantically grabs the bowl of popcorn and runs offstage.* STEF *watches him leave.*)

STEF. Finally! I get to have my chair!

(*She moves to the chair and begins to relax.*)

Hmm. (*She sniffs.*) Do I smell smoke? Naw, couldn't be.

(*She sits back. Two firemen come in and carry* STEF, *chair and all, offstage, as the curtain closes.*)

THE END

BIRDBRAIN VALENTINE

Characters

NARRATOR
BERTHA BIRD
BEULAH BIRD
BETTY BIRD
BONNY BIRD
BILLY BIRD
BENJAMIN BIRD

Setting the Stage

All characters are dressed as birds with beaks and wings. They might wear yellow and white clothes or leotards. BENJAMIN BIRD, however, wears weird colors, has "feathers" sticking straight up out of his tail, wears sunglasses, carries a radio, and flaps and dances around. You can make the beaks from construction paper and attach feathers (long strips of material or butcher paper) to sleeves and back. A sign at the back of the stage says "BIRD SANCTUARY."

SCENE. *At the bird sanctuary* BERTHA BIRD *and* BEULAH BIRD *are getting ready for Valentine's Day.*

NARRATOR. You may not know this, but Valentine's Day is the day the birds are supposed to choose their mates. Let's enter this bird community and see what's happening.

(BERTHA *and* BEULAH *stand together flapping their wings and talking excitedly.*)

BERTHA. Oh, I'm so excited! Today is Valentine's Day.

BEULAH. Me, too! I hope I get picked to be somebody's mate.

BERTHA. Get picked? Not me! (*Pointing to herself*) *I'm* doing the picking for this bird.

BEULAH. Oh, really, Bertha, you're too much!

(*They giggle.* BILLY BIRD *enters. He stands preening, flapping his "wings" and strutting, showing off.*)

BERTHA (*watching* BILLY). Oh, there's Billy Bird. Do you think he's watching us? He's the birdliest of them all! Don't you agree?

BEULAH. Oh, I don't know.

(*She looks doubtful.* BILLY *flaps his wings, showing off his strength and grace.*)

BERTHA. He has such fine feathers! I think he's the best hunk of birdmeat around.

BEULAH. I guess you're right. He *is* the birdliest!

(*She sighs loudly and stares at him.* BETTY BIRD *enters and stands by the other ladies.*)

BEULAH (*dreamily*). Isn't he just a dreambird? He has such a noble birdlike profile.

BETTY. Who?

BEULAH. Billy Bird. (*She sighs.*)

BETTY. Well, I suppose. . . .

BERTHA. He has such a sensitive beak, don't you think? (*She waves and* BILLY *waves back.*)

BETTY. Yes, I guess you're right. (*She sighs, too.*) He has such strong-looking birdlegs and such adorable webbed feet. I've never seen any webbier.

(BONNY BIRD *enters and joins them.*)

BONNY. Why are you just standing around? Don't you know what day this is? You should get busy!

BETTY. We *are* busy—watching him!

BONNY. Who?

BETTY. Billy Bird. Isn't he something to chirp about?

(BETTY, BEULAH *and* BERTHA *make bird noises and flap around as* BILLY *continues showing off.*)

BONNY. What are you birdbrains doing?

BEULAH. He's the birdliest!

BONNY (*thinks a moment and then answers*). I don't think he's the birdliest. I've seen better-looking birds than him in a badminton game.

BETTY (*disappointed*). You have?

BONNY. Yes, he has a real sappy-looking beak, if you ask me.

BERTHA. Really?

BONNY. Yes, and his feathers are dull and droopy-looking. And my goodness, look at those wimpy birdlegs!

BEULAH. Are you sure?

(BILLY *scrunches his shoulders, rejected.* BENJAMIN BIRD *enters. He's a ridiculous-looking bird. He stands next to* BILLY, *flapping, acting goofy and dancing.*)

BONNY (*to the other birds*). Now there's my idea of a real fowl!

BERTHA. Him? You're kidding, aren't you?

BONNY. No, I'm not. He's so much more original. Why, look at those outstanding tail feathers!

BERTHA (*unsure*). That's true—they do stand out.

BONNY. He's so interesting and unusual. Such form, such grace! Now that's real birdlike elegance!

BEULAH. Yes! You know, I think she's right!

BETTY. I've always thought Benjamin was the birdliest of them all!

BERTHA. Me, too! (*She sighs.*) He's mine!

BETTY & BEULAH. No, he's mine! I saw him first!

(BETTY, BEULAH *and* BERTHA *begin flapping, making bird noises to get* BENJAMIN*'s attention. He continues his "dance" unaware of them.*)

BONNY. Oh, brother!

(*The other birds are too busy to hear her.* BONNY *flutters over to* BILLY *and takes him by the wing. They flap offstage together while the other birds continue their fight over* BENJAMIN, *and the curtain closes.*)

THE END

Birdbrain Valentine ☆ 27

THE FIRST FLAG

Characters

BETSY ROSS
GEORGE WASHINGTON
MARTHA WASHINGTON

Setting the Stage

Characters could wear "powdered wigs" made from cotton balls. Ladies wear long dresses. GEORGE could wear knickers, white socks, a white shirt and a darker vest. Several flags are needed. You can make them from old sheets or construction paper. Descriptions of the flags are contained in the skit, but you can use any designs you want. Other props: Signs reading, "Several Months Later" and "A Couple of Days Later."

SCENE. BETSY ROSS's *house. She sits in a chair with her sewing materials scattered around her and the first flag on her lap. A box marked "Old Scraps" sits beside her chair.* GEORGE *and* MARTHA WASHINGTON *enter.*

GEORGE. Betsy, is the flag ready yet?

BETSY. Yes, and you're going to love it!

(*She holds up a bright green flag with yellow and purple flowers all over it.*)

GEORGE. Wonderful! It's exactly what I had in mind!

BETSY. Oh, thank you. I like it, too!

MARTHA. George, I don't think it's right.

GEORGE. Why not?

MARTHA. Well, what's it supposed to represent?

BETSY (*impatiently*). Well, the beauty of our country, of course.

MARTHA. George, I don't like it.

GEORGE (*meekly*). Well, maybe it isn't quite what we want. Why don't you try again, Betsy?

BETSY (*glaring at* MARTHA). All right, whatever you say.

(*She goes back to work. A sign, carried across the stage, says, "Several Months Later." * GEORGE *and* MARTHA *enter.*)

GEORGE. Well, Betsy, what do you have for us this time?

(BETSY *holds up a flag that's pink with a giant red heart. It has the white letters USA in the middle of the heart.*)

BETSY. Do you like this any better?

MARTHA. Oh, now that's really lovely!

GEORGE. I don't know. Somehow it doesn't grab me.

MARTHA. It really is nice, but I think maybe you should make a different one for the country. (*Taking the flag*) I have other plans for this one!

BETSY. Do you know how long it takes to make these things by hand—all the tedious effort it takes? I sure wish somebody would invent the sewing machine.

GEORGE. The what?

BETSY. Never mind, it was just a thought. I'll try again. Come back in another couple of months when I'm done.

MARTHA. I'm taking this one home with me to hang up in our den. It will be lovely with my new drapes!

(GEORGE *and* MARTHA *exit with* MARTHA *carrying the pink flag.* BETSY *goes back to her work. Again the sign is carried across the stage: "Several Months Later."* GEORGE *and* MARTHA *re-enter.*)

GEORGE. Well, Betsy, I hope this time you've come up with something our country can use.

(BETSY *holds up a white flag with five rings on it, just like the Olympic flag.*)

BETSY. I think it's nice, don't you?

GEORGE. Well, it does have definite possibilities, but I just don't think it would fit our needs.

MARTHA. I agree. It's just too sporty.

BETSY (*throws the flag at them*). Why don't you just make the flag yourself? I'm running out of ideas!

GEORGE. Just give it one more try and then if it isn't what we want, we'll find somebody else to do the job. Okay?

BETSY. Okay, okay—one more try.

(GEORGE *and* MARTHA *leave.* BETSY *looks at her sewing supplies and thinks a minute.*)

Oh, dear, I'm all out of material. I used it up on all my other failures. Now what will I do? (*She thinks.*) I guess I'll just have to find something from the scrap box to make into a flag. Hmm, let's see. (*She sorts through her scrap box.*) All I have left are my dad's old striped pajamas and an old navy uniform. This will never work! Oh, who cares? I'll just throw something together and show it to George and Martha. They'll hate it, and then they'll get off my back once and for all. Let's see, what kind of a flag can I make from striped pajamas and an old uniform? This ought to be interesting!

(*She sits and begins to work. A sign carried across the stage, says, "A Couple of Days Later."* GEORGE *and* MARTHA *enter.*)

GEORGE. We got a message that you wanted to see us. Why so soon? Have you thought of an idea for the new flag?

BETSY. Not exactly—I'm finished with it!

GEORGE. But you couldn't be. It usually takes you months to finish one. It's only been a couple of days now.

BETSY. Well, I am done. And don't forget, you said this could be my last try. You promised you'd ask somebody else to do a flag if you didn't like this one.

MARTHA. Okay, we will, but don't you think we should at least see the flag before we decide that we don't like it? Where is it?

BETSY. Well, okay. Here goes. Now don't you forget— it's my last try.

(*She holds up the first U.S. flag, red and white stripes, with a field of blue and a circle of thirteen stars.*)

GEORGE. It looks like somebody's old pajamas!

MARTHA. Oh, no, George, this is it! This is the one! Trust me on this—I'm never wrong. This flag is perfect!

BETSY. It is? Really?

MARTHA. Oh, yes, it's just right!

GEORGE. But, Martha . . .

MARTHA. Don't argue with me on this, George, or I'll hide your false teeth again.

GEORGE. Yes, dear. (*To* BETSY) We'll take the flag.

MARTHA. And Betsy Ross, you'll go down in history as the person who made the first flag of our great country!

BETSY. Oh, boy.

(BETSY *shakes her head and shrugs her shoulders as* GEORGE *and* MARTHA *leave with* MARTHA *proudly holding the flag. The curtain closes.*)

THE END

IF I WERE PRESIDENT . . .

Characters

JIMMY
KEVIN
VICE PRESIDENT

Setting the Stage

JIMMY and KEVIN could be dressed in suits and ties, but they also need bathrobes for the first scene. At first the stage is set up as a bedroom. During the dream it is supposed to look like the Oval Office of the President of the U.S. with desk, phone, flag, etc. Other props: Sign reading "Later."

SCENE. JIMMY*'s bedroom.* JIMMY *and* KEVIN *are getting ready for bed and discussing affairs of the nation.*

JIMMY. If I were president, boy, would I change this country.

KEVIN. What do you mean?

(*The boys get in their beds, still talking.*)

JIMMY. Well, I wouldn't make people pay so many taxes. And I'd make sure everyone had a job, and I'd give all kids ice-cream cones in their school lunches.

KEVIN. Wow, that sounds great! I wish you'd become president!

JIMMY. Yeah. (*He yawns.*) Me, too—me, too . . . If I were president. . . .

(*He falls asleep as the curtain closes. When the curtain reopens, we are in* JIMMY's *dream.* JIMMY *is sitting at his desk in the Oval Office, signing papers. In walks* KEVIN *with another pile.*)

KEVIN. Mr. President, here are some more papers for you to sign.

JIMMY. More? This is getting boring! All I ever get to do is sign papers! Doesn't the president get to do anything more fun than this?

KEVIN. I'm afraid not, sir.

JIMMY. Then I don't want to be president any more.

KEVIN. I'm sorry, sir, but you're in it for four years.

JIMMY. That's terrible! (*He thinks for a minute.*) Well, then, I'll just have to make it more interesting. Who do I call to install a basketball hoop?

KEVIN. Mr. President, not in the Oval Office!

JIMMY. I mean it! Who do I call?

KEVIN. The Secretary of Playground Equipment, I guess.

JIMMY. Okay, call him and tell him I want it here by tomorrow.

KEVIN. Yes, sir. (*He begins to leave.*)

JIMMY. Oh—and one more thing. I want a law giving all kids ice-cream cones for lunch every day. (*He picks up some of the papers on his desk, gets ready to sign them.*)

KEVIN. But sir, it would have to go through Congress. They'd never sign a bill giving every kid in the country free ice-cream cones for lunch!

JIMMY (*looking at the papers in front of him*). Is this the proposed budget?

KEVIN. Yes, sir, but about the ice cream—

JIMMY. You tell Congress I won't sign this until they sign a bill giving kids ice cream for lunch.

KEVIN. Yes, sir, I'll tell them. (*He shakes his head as he leaves.*)

(*The curtain closes. A sign carried across the stage reads "Later."*)

Well, sir, now that you passed your ice-cream cone bill, you seem to be very popular with young people.

JIMMY. That's nice.

KEVIN. Not really, because they can't vote and their parents don't like you too well.

JIMMY. Why not?

KEVIN. Maybe it's because you passed a bill outlawing homework. Or maybe it was your bill giving kids the authority over setting their own bedtimes.

JIMMY. That made the parents mad, huh? Oh, well, they'll get over it.

VICE PRESIDENT (*rushing in*). Mr. President, I hate to interrupt, but I have terrible news!

JIMMY. Who are you?

VICE PRESIDENT. I'm the Vice President, sir!

JIMMY. Oh, yeah. Go ahead then, what is it?

VICE PRESIDENT. Well, it's about this ice cream thing. Remember when I asked how we were going to pay for it since you lowered taxes?

JIMMY. Sure. I told them to take it out of our foreign-aid budget.

VICE PRESIDENT. Yes, you told them we needed it more than all those poor countries we were sending money to. And now those other countries are so mad at us that they've joined together and sent word that if we don't change our policy, they're going to declare a nuclear war against us.

JIMMY. Oh, no, we can't fight a nuclear war.

KEVIN. Why not?

JIMMY. I used all our defense money to start my Send-a-Kid-to-Disneyland program.

KEVIN. You used all of it?

JIMMY. Yeah, there are a lot of kids in this country!

VICE PRESIDENT. They're going to attack tomorrow! What will we do?

JIMMY. Well—uh—gee, I don't know—

KEVIN. You're the president—DO SOMETHING!

JIMMY. Help! (*He begins to cry as the curtain closes.*)

(*The curtain opens with* KEVIN *sitting on* JIMMY'*s bed shaking him.* JIMMY *is still yelling "Help!"*)

JIMMY (*leaping up*). Huh? Where am I? Have they attacked yet?

KEVIN. What are you talking about? You must have had a bad dream.

JIMMY. Boy, I'll say. I'm glad it was just a dream. I'm okay now. Let's go back to sleep. (*They get back into their beds.*) Hey, Kevin? You remember when I was talking about if I were president?

KEVIN (*sleepily*). Uh-huh.

JIMMY. I changed my mind. I don't think I *ever* want to be president.

KEVIN. Okay—then I won't vote for you. Now good night!

JIMMY. Good night.

(*The curtain closes.*)

THE END

THE PEOPLE AGAINST GEORGE WASHINGTON

Characters

GEORGE WASHINGTON
GEORGE'S LAWYER (LAWYER #1)
MRS. BRADLEY
MRS. BRADLEY'S LAWYER (LAWYER #2)
JUDGE
BAILIFF
JURY
GUARDS

Setting the Stage

Actors can dress in knickers with white shirts and vests. You can make "powdered wigs" from cotton balls or have the actors pull their hair back in ponytails. JUDGE wears a long robe and carries a gavel. Mrs. Bradley's lawyer needs an ax that can be made from cardboard.

SCENE. *In the courtroom,* JUDGE *is seated at a raised desk center stage. On one side are* GEORGE *and his lawyer.* GUARDS *stand on either side of* GEORGE. *At the other side are* MRS. BRADLEY *and her lawyer.* JURY *is seated in chairs along one side of the stage.*

JUDGE (*pounds his gavel*). Are we ready to begin the next case?

LAWYERS. Yes, Your Honor.

JUDGE (*reading*). The next case is "The People versus George Washington." Mr. Plaintiff, could we please hear your opening statement?

LAWYER #2. Yes, Your Honor. We will prove without a doubt that Mrs. Bradley's prize cherry tree was maliciously chopped down. And furthermore, we intend to prove that the culprit who chopped it was none other than young Master George Washington.

GEORGE. I'm innocent! (*He begins to move towards the bench, but guards restrain him.*)

JUDGE (*pounds gavel*). Order! You'll get your turn later. Now, may we please hear the defendant's opening remarks?

LAWYER #1. Yes, Your Honor. Well, personally I think the little scamp did it, too, but he claims he's innocent, so I guess we'll try to prove that.

JUDGE. Now will the plaintiff please call his first witness?

LAWYER #2. Yes, I call Mrs. Bradley.

(MRS. BRADLEY *takes the stand.*)

BAILIFF. Raise your right hand. Do you swear to tell the truth, the whole truth, and nothing but the truth, so help you God?

MRS. BRADLEY. I do.

BAILIFF. Be seated.

LAWYER #2. Mrs. Bradley, please tell the court in your own words what you saw last Saturday morning.

MRS. BRADLEY. Well, I was busy making breakfast, and I heard a terrible noise, so I looked outside and saw my prize cherry tree toppling over. And then I noticed a young man standing next to it with an ax.

LAWYER #2. Is this the ax you later found lying next to your tree? (*He holds up cardboard ax.*)

MRS. BRADLEY. Yes, I believe it is.

LAWYER #2. I'd like to submit this ax as evidence. Notice that the handle is engraved with the initials, "G. W."

GEORGE. This is a set-up!

JUDGE. Order in this courtroom! Young man, you must be quiet now or I'll charge you with contempt of court. Now you may proceed.

LAWYER #2. Now, Mrs. Bradley, is the person you saw next to your beloved cherry tree in this courtroom today?

MRS. BRADLEY. Well, I'm not sure, but maybe.

LAWYER #2. Will you kindly point him out to the court?

MRS. BRADLEY. Well, it might have been him. (*She points to* GEORGE.)

LAWYER #2. Are you sure?

MRS. BRADLEY. Well, I think so. My eyes aren't too good, you know. But yes, I do believe it was him.

LAWYER #2. No further questions.

JUDGE (*to* LAWYER #1). Any cross-examination?

LAWYER #1. No questions, Your Honor.

GEORGE (*outraged*). How do you expect to help me if you don't ask any questions?

LAWYER #1. I'm not sure yet. I'm thinking.

JUDGE. Okay, Plaintiff, you may call your next witness.

LAWYER #2. The prosecution rests, Your Honor.

JUDGE. All right, Defense, you may present your case.

LAWYER #1. What case?

JUDGE. You know, you said you'd try to prove his innocence.

LAWYER #1. Oh, yeah, that. Well, I guess I could call George Washington to the stand.

(GEORGE *takes the stand.*)

BAILIFF. Raise your right hand. Do you swear to tell the truth, the whole truth and nothing but the truth, so help you God?

GEORGE. I do.

BAILIFF. Be seated.

LAWYER #1. Now, George, tell us the truth this time. Did you chop down that cherry tree?

GEORGE. I'm innocent, I tell you—I'm innocent!

LAWYER #1 (*to* JUDGE). Your Honor, I can see we're not getting anywhere here. May I have a word with my client?

JUDGE. Yes, but make it short.

(GEORGE *and* LAWYER #1 *come to the front of the stage to talk. Their backs are to the rest of the courtroom.*)

LAWYER #1. Look, Georgie, he's got a witness saying she saw you. He's got an ax with your initials on it. You don't have an alibi, and it's pretty clear that you did chop down that stupid cherry tree. Why don't you just tell the truth and throw yourself on the mercy of the court?

GEORGE. But what if I really am innocent?

LAWYER #1. It won't matter. The jury will believe her story anyway, and you'll still be found guilty. If you plead guilty, you'll get off easier.

GEORGE. What will happen to me if I plead guilty?

LAWYER #1. You'll get a lighter sentence, and people will look up to you for being honest. You may get a good reputation. Who knows, someday you may even grow up to be president.

GEORGE. What's a president?

LAWYER #1. Well, he's the leader of a country.

GEORGE. But the king of England is the leader of our colonies!

LAWYER #1. Never mind, we're wasting time. If you tell the jury you did it, you probably won't have to go to jail.

GEORGE. Well, okay, if you really think it's the best way.

(GEORGE *goes back to the witness stand.*)

JUDGE. Are you ready now?

GEORGE. Yes, Your Honor. (*To* JURY) I cannot tell a lie! I *did* chop down the cherry tree! (*He crosses his fingers behind his back.*)

LAWYER #1. The defense rests, Your Honor.

JUDGE. Jury, are you ready for the verdict?

(JURY *confers noisily.*)

HEAD JURYMAN. Yes, Your Honor. We find the defendant guilty as charged. But since he did step forward and confess, we would like to recommend a lighter sentence.

JUDGE. I'm ready to pronounce sentence. George Washington, I hereby sentence you to a life term of community service.

GEORGE. A life term? For one measly cherry tree? That's not fair! I already have my life all planned out. I'm going to be an interior decorator!

JUDGE. Sorry, not any more you aren't. You will dedicate all your time to helping your country. The case is closed! (*He pounds his gavel.*)

GEORGE (*to his lawyer*). What kind of a democracy is this anyway?

LAWYER #1. What's a democracy?

GEORGE. I've been set up! I want to change my plea! It's not fair!

(GUARDS *pick him up and begin to carry him away kicking and screaming.*)

Put me down! I tell you, I'm innocent!

(*The curtain closes.*)

THE END

Skits &
Sketches
for Spring

THE LEPRECHAUN

Characters

PETER
MICHAEL
LEPRECHAUN

Setting the Stage

PETER and MICHAEL need no special costumes. LEPRECHAUN could wear green clothes, have a green cotton beard and a little green hat. The background could be made to look like a forest with trees and rocks. Behind one rock in the middle of the stage is a small pile of pennies.

SCENE. *Forest.* PETER *and* MICHAEL *enter, holding an old handwritten map.*

PETER. I'm not kidding. According to the map, this is the exact spot where a leprechaun was spotted a hundred years ago.

MICHAEL. Where did you get that map?

PETER. From a book. It also said that leprechauns return every hundred years.

MICHAEL. So what do we do now?

PETER. We just wait. And when he comes back, we catch him. If you catch a leprechaun, he has to grant you three wishes.

MICHAEL (*doubtfully*). Okay, whatever you say.

(*The boys sit and wait.* LEPRECHAUN *enters sneakily. They spot him.*)

PETER. There he is! See, I told you so!

MICHAEL. Amazing! You were right!

PETER. Now, let's catch him!

(*They begin to chase* LEPRECHAUN *around the stage. Finally they catch him.*)

MICHAEL. We did it!

LEPRECHAUN. Let go of me, you obnoxious creatures!

PETER. Only if you promise not to run away. You have to give us three wishes. It said so in the book.

LEPRECHAUN. All right, all right, you win. You'll have your three wishes. But you can only have three; so think carefully. And you can't wish for a thousand other wishes.

PETER. Wow, now what do we wish for? A million dollars? A mountain of ice cream? All the toys in the world? This is going to be tough.

LEPRECHAUN. Be careful. Sometimes when you wish for something, you're surprised by the results.

MICHAEL. We have to think carefully now. Maybe we could each have one wish for ourselves and then share the other. What do you think?

LEPRECHAUN. Be careful. I'm warning you.

PETER. Yeah. That sounds okay to me.

LEPRECHAUN. Think hard now—don't be hasty.

MICHAEL. Should I go first, or do you want to?

LEPRECHAUN. Don't be greedy, and don't decide too quickly.

PETER. I'll go first. Let's see, what do I wish for?

LEPRECHAUN. Don't forget, be really careful!

PETER (*to* LEPRECHAUN). I wish you'd shut up so I can think!

LEPRECHAUN. Very well, that's your first wish—be granted!

(LEPRECHAUN *stands silently. The boys realize what's happened.*)

MICHAEL. Now look what you've done! You wasted a whole wish. Now we only have two.

PETER. Oh, well, that's still one for each of us.

MICHAEL. No, sir, that was your wish you wasted! I have a wish and we have one to share.

PETER. Don't argue. I'm the one that found him, aren't I? I could have used all the wishes myself.

MICHAEL. Okay, go ahead and make your wish.

PETER. Okay, I wish for a million dollars.

(LEPRECHAUN *shrugs his shoulders, shakes his head, and points to his mouth.*)

PETER. What's wrong? My second wish is for a million dollars.

MICHAEL. It looks like he can't grant it unless he can talk. And you wished for him to shut up!

PETER. Well, we'll just have to wish for him to talk again. (*He turns to* LEPRECHAUN.) I wish you'd talk again.

LEPRECHAUN. Wish—be granted. Okay, what'll it be for your last wish?

MICHAEL. This one is mine!

PETER. No, we have to share.

MICHAEL. But you wasted our other wishes.

PETER. But if it weren't for my map, you wouldn't even be here. Come on, let's wish for a million dollars and we'll share it.

MICHAEL. Okay, I guess you're right. But why a million? Why not two or twenty—or a hundred million? Then we'd have more.

PETER. True. What's the highest number you can think of? Hmmm. I know! Let's wish for a mountain of money. That will be more than we could ever count!

MICHAEL. I don't know. He said we shouldn't be too greedy.

PETER. Yes, we should. (*He turns to* LEPRECHAUN.) I wish for a mountain of money!

LEPRECHAUN. Wish—be granted! It's over there—just move that rock out of the way.

PETER. But there's no mountain over there.

LEPRECHAUN. Yes, there is. Go see for yourself.

(MICHAEL *moves the rock. Behind it is a small pile of pennies.*)

MICHAEL. But it's just a pile of pennies!

LEPRECHAUN. You didn't say how big a mountain. That is what you asked for—a mountain of money. Now I have to be going. Don't worry, I'll be back in another hundred years. Then—if you're still fast enough to catch me—you can have another three wishes. But next time be more careful!

(*He exits. The boys drop to the ground crying and kicking their legs and arms as the curtain closes.*)

THE END

THE LUCKY CLOVER

Characters
MAN
OLD LADY
TWO POLICE OFFICERS
YOUNG WOMAN

Setting the Stage
MAN may wish to wear a suit and tie. OLD LADY could wear a shawl and a long dress. She carries a purse. POLICE OFFICERS wear hats and carry guns. The young woman carries a bag of garbage. A large four-leaf clover made from paper is needed. Other props: Crutches, and a sign reading "Later."

SCENE. MAN *is walking along the street. He sees a four-leaf clover and picks it up.*

MAN. Oh, boy! It's a four-leaf clover! I can't believe it! How lucky! I've never even seen one of these before. I'll just put it in my pocket. It's sure to bring me good luck.

(*He walks along humming.* OLD LADY *enters, crashes into him. They fall to the ground.*)

MAN. Are you all right? You really should watch where you're going.

OLD LADY. Me? Why, you ran right into me.

MAN. Oh, no, ma'am, you ran into me.

OLD LADY. You young whippersnapper, I'll teach you not to run into defenseless old women!

(*She hits him over the head with purse, chasing him around stage.* POLICE OFFICERS *enter.*)

POLICEMAN #1. Stop that!

(*The* POLICEMEN *break up the fight.*)

What's going on here?

OLD LADY. He ran me down and tried to steal my purse.

MAN. No, officers, I simply—

POLICEMAN #2. Don't argue, punk, we're taking you to jail.

MAN. Jail! But, sir, I—

(*They each take an arm and whisk him offstage. A sign, carried across the stage, reads "Later."* MAN *comes trudging across the stage.*)

MAN. What an experience! That was terrible! I've never had such an awful time in my life. I'm glad they finally let me out on bail.

(YOUNG WOMAN *comes by with a bag of garbage.*)

WOMAN. This looks like a good place to dump my garbage.

(*She dumps it right on him and then leaves. The police return. The man is cleaning himself off.*)

POLICEMAN #1. So it's you again! Dumping garbage all over the streets! That's littering! Don't you know that will be a $100 fine? We'll have to write you a ticket. (*They do.*) Now go home and stay there!

(Exit POLICEMEN.)

MAN Oh, brother! What else could go wrong?

(*He trips, falls over some of the garbage and hurts his ankle badly. Now he has trouble walking.*)

I'm going home! But first I'm getting rid of this unlucky four-leaf clover. I've had nothing but bad luck since I found it.

(*He throws it on the ground and limps off.* YOUNG WOMAN *returns and finds the clover.*)

WOMAN. Oh, look, a four-leaf clover! How lucky! I've never even seen one before. I bet it brings me luck.

(*She exits. A sign carried across the stage reads "Later."* MAN *returns on crutches.* YOUNG WOMAN *runs in screaming and yelling, knocks him down.*)

I won, I won, I won!

MAN. What did you win? (*He stands up.*)

WOMAN. I just won a million dollars, and I owe it all to my lucky four-leaf clover! (*She kisses it.*)

MAN. *Your* four-leaf clover?

LADY. Yes, I found it right here, and ever since I've had nothing but great luck!

(*She runs offstage.* MAN *slumps to the ground and begins to cry as the curtain closes.*)

THE END

APRIL FOOL FOR NEXT YEAR

Characters
MRS. WILLIS (teacher)
MR. SNIDER (gym teacher)
STUDENTS

Setting the Stage
The stage is set up as a classroom. Teachers may wish to wear appropriate clothing (such as longer dress, high heels, suit, tie). Students need an assortment of props for practical jokes (such as whoopee cushion, shaving cream, bucket of water, fake spiders and snakes, Oreo cookies). Other props: pie plates filled with shaving cream and a sign reading "The Next Morning."

SCENE. *A classroom.* MRS. WILLIS *enters and speaks to the audience.*

MRS. WILLIS (*sweetly*). Hello, everyone. (*She looks at her watch.*) Oh, no. It's just about time for those little brats—er, uh, I mean my students—to come back from the gym. Oh, well, I'm prepared for those monsters. They haven't fooled me yet, and I'm not about to let them. (*She holds up a box of assorted practical joke items.*) I've spent the whole day dodging their little April Fools' Day tricks. This is quite a collection, isn't it? I'm just glad the day is almost over so I can get rid of those—er—students—for a little while, and get rid of April Fools' Day for another year. Uh-oh! Here come those terribly—er, uh—sweet things now.

(*The class files in and sits down. Next, in walks* MR. SNIDER, *the gym teacher, with shaving cream all over him.*)

MRS. WILLIS. Oh, hello, Mr. Snider. How was gym today?

MR. SNIDER (*looking at his clothing*). Not bad—pretty mild, I'd say. (*He shrugs his shoulders and shakes his head.*)

MRS. WILLIS. You've got to get tough, man. You have to be smart. You can't let these little fools get the best of you!

MR. SNIDER. Whatever you say.

MRS. WILLIS. Don't be such a wimp. You'd never catch *me* getting fooled by a bunch of amateurs like them. (*She points to her class.*)

MR. SNIDER. I'll try.

(*He leaves.* STUDENTS *begin to put their books away as if getting ready to go home.*)

STUDENT #1. Mrs. Willis, it's time to go home. Look at the clock!

MRS. WILLIS. Well, that's funny. (*She looks puzzled for a moment, checks her watch, then checks the classroom clock.*) Oh, you little scamps! You're not going to fool me with that old turning-the-clock-ahead gag! I've been teaching too long to fall for that one.

STUDENT #2. Mrs. Willis, you're no fun. We haven't caught you yet!

MRS. WILLIS. I know, and you aren't going to, either. I pride myself on outsmarting you practical jokers.

(*The students groan, obviously defeated. One student tries to sneak up behind her with a bucket of water. She turns quickly and intercepts it.*)

Oh, thank you, Mark—you brought some water. It's awfully nice of you to offer to clean the blackboards—after school!

(*She smiles as* MARK *slinks back to his seat.*)

I'm too smart for you all. Just give up!

STUDENT #3. Okay, you win, Mrs. Willis. You *are* too smart for us. Here, have a cookie as a token of my esteem.

(STUDENT #3 *hands her an Oreo cookie.*)

MRS. WILLIS. Why, thank you. That's awfully nice of you.

(*Some of the students are grinning, preparing for their victory. She sees that they are planning something.*)

But I'm on a diet. I have to watch my figure, you know. Here, Mark, since you so generously offered to clean the boards for me, you can eat it.

MARK. Gee, thanks! (*He stuffs the whole thing into his mouth and then spits it out.*) Yuck! It's got toothpaste inside!

MRS. WILLIS (*with mock surprise*). Oh, really? Now, class, get busy on your math assignment while I correct some papers.

(*She moves towards her desk. Some students giggle. She begins to sit. They cover their mouths, trying not to laugh. Just as she's about to sit, she stops, checks her chair, picks up a whoopee cushion and holds it in the air.*)

MRS. WILLIS. Thank you to whoever did this. I'll add it to my collection. (*She puts it in the box.*) I should be able to open up my own practical joke shop soon with all your lovely contributions.

(*She picks up a rubber snake and throws it into the box.*)

Just what I needed to make my collection complete!

(*The class groans. Just then the bell rings.*)

Class dismissed. Oh, and don't forget your fifty-page homework assignment.

(*The class leaves amid moans and groans.*)

Hooray! It's over! I must say, they weren't much of a challenge this year.

(*She puts her feet up on the desk, leans back, and*

relaxes with a smug look on her face as the curtain closes. A sign, carried across the stage, says "The Next Morning." In walks MRS. WILLIS, *all bright and cheery, humming to herself.*)

MRS. WILLIS. What a beautiful day! Spring is here, and I don't have to worry about April Fools' Day for another whole year!

(*The bell rings. Students enter.*)

Good morning, class. Now I'd like you all to turn in your homework.

STUDENT #1. Are you sure?

MRS. WILLIS (*impatiently*). Of course. (*She holds out her hand.*) Let's have it, class. I can't wait all day!

STUDENT #2. Okay, everybody, let's let her have it!

(*They all reach under their desks and get out pie plates filled with shaving cream. They all throw them at her, covering her with shaving cream. She stands there, stunned.*)

MRS. WILLIS. But, but, but—

CLASS (*yells*). APRIL FOOL FOR NEXT YEAR!

(MRS. WILLIS *faints, and the curtain closes.*)

THE END

MIXED NUTS

Characters
PHIL
GIL
BILL
WILL
DILL
HAL
SAL
HUBERT

Note: *This sketch may be done with all girls or all boys or mixed girls and boys. For girls' names, you could use Lil and Jill, Tyl and Syl, Val and Sal, and Gladys.*

Setting the Stage
The "nuts" are dressed oddly in mismatched clothes, odd color combinations and strange hats. HUBERT needs no special costume.

SCENE. *It is April Fools' Day. The "nuts" are at home, all on stage, except for* HUBERT. *They are standing around talking.*

PHIL. Hi, Bill. Hello, Dill.

BILL. Hello, Phil. How's it going, Will?

WILL. Just fine, Bill. How are you, Gil?

GIL. Not bad, Will. How about you, Sal?

SAL. I'm fine, Gil. What are you doing, Hal?

HAL. I'm trying to remember what day it is. Let's see.

(He has four hats on his head. As he takes each one off, he counts off the months.) January, February, March, April. Oh, yeah, it's April.

PHIL. How do you know that?

HAL. I can tell by my hats. Today is April first.

WILL. Oh, boy, April Fools' Day! My favorite day of the year!

BILL. Let's play a joke on somebody.

DILL. Good idea, but who? We're all here. Who should we play it on?

GIL. I saw Hubert outside. Why don't we call him in and play a joke on him?

PHIL. Good idea. But what joke can we play?

WILL. We could all stand on our heads and act like it was totally normal and make him think he was upside down.

(They try standing on their heads and fall over. Finally they give up.)

HAL. This won't work. Why don't we just hide and he'll come in and think he's alone. Then we can all jump out and yell April Fool!

SAL. Great idea!

(They all rush to find places to hide. The places are ridiculous because they can easily be seen sticking out behind or under furniture. Some pick very small things to hide behind.)

DILL. Is everybody ready?

EVERYONE. Yeah!

BILL. Oh, Hubert! Come in here!

(HUBERT enters and quickly notices everyone hiding.)

HUBERT. Hi, guys. How's it going?

(They come out of hiding disappointedly.)

PHIL *(jumping out)*. April Fool!

HUBERT. You didn't fool me. I saw you hiding.

SAL. Oh, rats, you're no fun. All seven of us were going to hide and jump out and scare you.

HAL *(begins counting)*. Hey, there's somebody missing.

(He counts everyone except HUBERT and himself.)

One, two, three, four, five, six. See? Somebody's still hiding!

GIL. Naw, we're all here. Watch—I'll count.

(*He counts everyone except Hubert and himself.*)

One, two, three, four, five, six. You're right! Somebody is still hiding. Let's find him.

HUBERT. But, guys . . .

(*Everyone begins looking for the missing person. HUBERT stands at the side shaking his head. After a while they give up.*)

PHIL. I can't find anyone. But somebody was missing. It's a mystery to me. Maybe he's in the Twilight Zone.

DILL. Or the Bermuda Triangle.

(*He scratches his head. The others look confused. Finally HUBERT comes forward.*)

HUBERT. There's nobody missing. I was trying to tell you that.

BILL. Yes, there is. We started with seven guys and now there're only six. You saw us count. Somebody's missing and we have to find him. I'll call the police.

HUBERT. You don't need the police. I'll find the missing person. Everyone line up.

(*They line up, as they say their names.*)

PHIL. Let's see. I'm Phil.

GIL. You're Phil, and I'm Gil.

BILL. Well, I know I'm Bill.

WILL (*points to others*). Phil, Gill, Bill, and I'm Will.

DILL. I guess I'm Dill.

HAL. I'm pretty sure I'm Hal.

SAL. Then I must be Sal!

HUBERT. Now, I'll count. One, two, three, four, five, six, seven. See? You're all here.

GIL. You're a genius!

WILL. You found the missing person!

HUBERT. No, I'm—you see, I'm—you just—I'm—

DILL. We're indebted to you forever.

HAL. And to think we wanted to play an April Fools' joke on you.

SAL. I feel terrible about that.

HUBERT. Oh, forget it! I give up trying to explain to this group of mixed nuts. You guys are the biggest April Fools of all.

(*He exits.*)

PHIL. I wonder what he meant by that?

(*The curtain closes.*)

THE END

JAIL BUNNY

Characters

EASTER BUNNY
TWO POLICE OFFICERS
OLD LADY

Setting the Stage

EASTER BUNNY could wear a full costume or just ordinary clothes plus bunny ears and a tail. He carries an Easter basket full of eggs and candy. He also has a carrot in his pocket. POLICE OFFICERS may wear caps and carry guns. OLD LADY could wear a shawl, a long dress and eyeglasses. She carries a purse.

SCENE. *The street in front of a house.* EASTER BUNNY *is getting ready to drop off a basket.*

BUNNY. Hi! You all know me, right? I'm the Easter Bunny. Since tomorrow is Easter, I'm here to do my yearly rounds, delivering Easter eggs and candies to all the little kiddies. Well, enough chit-chat, back to work!

(*He tries to open the door of the house, but can't.*)

Uh-oh, it's locked. I wish all the moms and dads would leave their doors unlocked just for this one night. I guess they're afraid of burglars. But how am I supposed to get in? I could just leave, but I don't want to let down the children who are expecting me tonight. If I don't leave this basket, those kids will never believe in me again. Hmmm. (*He scratches his head.*) Maybe I can pick the lock. (*He fiddles with it until it opens.*) There we go! Now I can do my job.

(POLICE OFFICERS *run in.*)

OFFICER #1. Freeze! Police! (EASTER BUNNY *freezes.*)

OFFICER #2. All right, you bozo, we caught you red-handed!

BUNNY. Who, me? I'm afraid you've got it all wrong, sirs. I'm the Easter Bunny.

OFFICER #1. Sure you are. And I'm King Kong and my partner is Superman. Now, up with your hands!

(EASTER BUNNY *puts his hands up. They frisk him.*)

OFFICER #2. Aha! I found the weapon, sir. It's here in his pocket. (*He pulls out a carrot.*)

OFFICER #1. That's a carrot, you numskull!

OFFICER #2. Well, uh, it felt like a gun or something. Sorry. I guess he's clean—well, pretty clean.

OFFICER #1. Okay, cuff him. We're going to take him down to the station for questioning.

BUNNY. But you can't.

(*They glare at him.*)

Well, I mean, I suppose you can, but if you do, I won't be able to finish my deliveries.

OFFICER #2. Don't you mean robberies?

BUNNY. No, I'm serious, officers! I *am* the Easter Bunny!

OFFICER #1. Yeah, yeah, that's what they all say. Don't you realize any crazy person can rent a rabbit suit and do what you doing?

BUNNY. I assure you, my suit is not rented. It's the original. I've had it since I was born.

OFFICER #2. You've got to be kidding! It isn't even a good imitation. Why, these dumb whiskers . . . (*he pulls them.*)

BUNNY. Ouch! Stop that!

OFFICER #1. And the ears! Charley, did you get a look at those ears?

(*They both laugh.*)

Come on, buddy, it's time to take the costume off.

(*They pull and tug, but can't get it off.*)

Hey, Charley, are you thinking what I'm thinking?

OFFICER #2. Yeah, this suit is the real thing! That must mean he *is* the real Easter Bunny. Gee, sorry. We didn't mean to give you such a hard time. It's just that we see so many weirdos in our line of work. You understand, don't you?

BUNNY. It's okay—no harm done. Can I go now?

OFFICER #1. Yeah, sure, go on and finish your work. Come on, let's go catch some real crooks.

(*They exit.*)

BUNNY. I'm really getting fed up. Sometimes I want to retire and start a carrot farm in southern California. Oh, well, I guess I'll finish my deliveries for this year, anyway.

(*He enters the house with his basket. A loud scream is heard from offstage.*)

OLD LADY (*offstage*). Help, police! I'm being robbed!

BUNNY (*runs across the stage*). Oh, no, not again!

(*He runs around the stage being chased by* OLD LADY, *who hits him with her purse.*)

OLD LADY. I'll teach you to break in and scare defenseless old ladies' you carrot-eating mongrel, you!

(*She chases him around the stage, waving her purse as the curtain closes.*)

THE END

HOW TO MAKE THE TEAM

Characters
CONRAD
ZACHARY
VOICE OFFSTAGE

Setting the Stage

CONRAD needs a baseball hat, mitt and bat. ZACHARY needs an assortment of props including cans of vegetables, a karate suit, a ballet skirt or toe shoes, a jogging suit and a rope. Other props: Signs reading, "Later," "Still Later," "Almost Tryout Day" and "After Tryouts."

SCENE. *At home.* ZACHARY *sits at the table with a pile of cans of vegetables in front of him.* CONRAD *enters, carrying a mitt, bat and ball.*

CONRAD. What are you doing?

ZACHARY. I'm going to eat all these vegetables so I can be healthy.

CONRAD. Yech! I like candy bars better!

ZACHARY. I used to, too, but now I'm into asparagus, brussels sprouts, beets, cauliflower, spinach. I've got it all.

(*He holds up cans of vegetables.*)

CONRAD. Why are you so into vegetables now?

ZACHARY. Because you have to be really healthy to make the team.

CONRAD. What team?

ZACHARY. The baseball team! Tryouts are in a couple of weeks. After I eat all these vegetables I'll be super-healthy and ready to try out.

CONRAD. Okay, whatever you say. I'm gonna go play ball now. (*He holds up his mitt and ball.*) You wanna come?

ZACHARY. No, I don't have time. I have to finish eating all these vegetables.

(*He points to the cans in front of him.*)

CONRAD. But that'll take days!

ZACHARY. I know, but just think how healthy I'll be!

(CONRAD *exits. The curtain closes. A sign, carried across the stage, reads "Later." When the curtain opens,* ZACH *is dressed in a combination of karate suit and ballet outfit. For example, he might wear the karate outfit with a tutu around his middle or with toe shoes. He is dancing around like a ballet dancer. Every so often he stops and does some karate kicks and chops into the air.* CONRAD *enters, and stares at* ZACHARY *with disbelief.*)

CONRAD. What in the world are you doing now?

ZACHARY. I call it "balletrate." It's a mixture of ballet (*he does a pirouette*) and karate (*he does some kicks*).

CONRAD. But why would you want to do something as ridic—er—I mean, unusual—as that?

ZACHARY. Ballet gives you grace and karate gives you strength. Since I didn't have time to learn both before baseball tryouts, I decided to mix them together.

CONRAD. You're still worried about baseball tryouts?

ZACHARY. Well, you have to be strong and graceful to be a baseball player. (*He continues his moves.*) And that's just what I plan to be.

CONRAD. Well, do you want to stop for a while and go play baseball? A few of the guys are—

ZACHARY. Sorry, I have too much to do.

(CONRAD *exits. The curtain closes and a sign, carried across the stage, reads "Still later." As the curtain reopens,* CONRAD *enters carrying his baseball gear.*)

CONRAD. Zach? Where is he now? I guess he isn't home yet.

(ZACHARY *comes tearing in and falls into a chair, exhausted.*)

VOICE OFFSTAGE (*yells*). Next time I'll get you!

CONRAD. What was that all about?

ZACHARY (*panting*). Oh, just part of my plan.

CONRAD. Part of your plan? What do you mean?

ZACHARY. Well, I needed to work on improving my speed, so I got Jimmy Benson to chase me home.

CONRAD. You mean *the* Jimmy Benson, the school bully? How did you get him to chase you home?

ZACHARY. Easy. I just told him his mother must be a pretty good weightlifter to have raised a big dumbbell like him!

CONRAD. You told Jimmy Benson that? Man, if he'd have caught you, you'd be dead meat!

ZACHARY. Yeah, I know. I wanted to improve my speed, and I figured the fear would help me. You have to be really fast to make the team, you know.

CONRAD. Why don't you just go play on the freeway? That would improve your speed, too!

ZACHARY. Hmmm—not a bad idea.

CONRAD. Oh, brother! I'm going to play ball with the guys.

(*He exits. The curtain closes. A sign carried across the stage, reads, "Almost Tryout Day." The curtain opens as* ZACHARY *holds a rope, trying to figure out what to do.* CONRAD *enters.*)

ZACHARY (*to himself*). Hmm—maybe I could—

CONRAD. What's up now?

ZACHARY. I'm trying to figure out how I can hang myself upside down. If I just tie this to my feet, maybe I can. . . . Maybe you can help me.

CONRAD. You're crazy! You'll kill yourself! Why do you want to hang upside down, anyway?

ZACHARY. I don't have much time left before tryouts. I heard if you hang upside down the blood will rush to your head and enrich your brain cells.

CONRAD. So? What does that have to do with tryouts?

ZACHARY. You're so stupid. I'm trying to get really smart. You have to be really smart to make the team. Now will you help me?

CONRAD. Forget it. Kill yourself if you want. I'm going to play ball with my friends.

ZACHARY (*throwing the rope away*). Maybe I'll just stand on my head.

(*He does, as the curtain closes.*)

I feel smarter already!

(*A sign, carried across the stage, reads "After Tryouts." The curtain opens.* ZACHARY *trudges in.*)

ZACHARY. I can't believe it. I didn't make the team! After all my hard work, I got cut!!

(*He falls to the ground sadly.* CONRAD *comes running onstage, jumping around ecstatically.*)

CONRAD. Guess what? I made the team!!! (*He runs back offstage.*)

ZACHARY. Where did I go wrong? Whaaa!!!

(*He throws himself down, kicking his arms and legs as the curtain closes.*)

THE END

Skits &
Sketches
for Autumn

THE GHOSTCATCHERS

Characters

MRS. BEAZLEY
TOM
HARRY
GHOST

Setting the Stage

GHOST needs a sheet for a costume. The ghostcatchers can be dressed in regular clothing. They need at least the following props: two monster masks, a rope, and a guitar. GHOST needs a suitcase, a newspaper, two couch pillows, sheets and pillowcases. Other props: two telephones; sign: "Eight hours later."

SCENE. MRS. BEAZLEY *is on the phone.* TOM *is downstage at another telephone answering her.*

MRS. BEAZLEY. Hello. Is this the company that catches ghosts?

TOM. Why, yes, it is.

MRS. BEAZLEY. Well, I'm calling because there's a ghost in my house, and he's scaring me to death. Could you please come exterminate him for me?

TOM. We'll try. Actually, you're our first customer. But don't worry, we'll figure out a way to get rid of him.

MRS. BEAZLEY. Oh, thank goodness! Hurry over. My house is at 801 Vapor Avenue.

TOM. We'll be right over. (*He hangs up.*) Hey, Harry, come here! We've actually got a customer!

(HARRY *enters.*)

HARRY. A customer? You mean somebody out there actually believes in ghosts?

TOM. Not just believes in them, but has one in her house. Our job is to go in there and get rid of it.

HARRY. A real ghost? That reminds me—did you ever come up with a plan for how to get rid of ghosts?

TOM. Me? That was your job! Remember, I was in charge of getting us the customers. Well, I got us a customer. Now the rest is up to you.

HARRY. Me? But I—

TOM. Don't worry. It can't be that hard to get rid of one little ghost. Come on, we'll think of something on the way over.

(They rush off and enter again backstage near Mrs. Beazley's house.)

HARRY. Well, here we are. *(He rings doorbell.)*

MRS. BEAZLEY. Thank goodness you're here! The ghost is inside. When you get rid of him, call me at this number. I can't take it any more!

(She rushes offstage.)

TOM *(motions to* HARRY *to enter first).* After you.

HARRY. I'm not going in first. This whole business was your idea. *You* go first.

TOM. Oh, all right. Let's get busy.

(They enter the living room. GHOST *is doing exercises off to one side.)*

HARRY. There he is. Okay, now what do we do?

TOM. I was thinking maybe we could scare him out.

(He hands HARRY *a monster mask and puts one on himself. They run around screaming and roaring, trying to scare* GHOST. GHOST *watches them and when they are all done he laughs and claps.)*

HARRY. That idea didn't work. How about if we tie a rope around him and pull him out?

TOM. Okay, we'll give it a try.

(They begin chasing GHOST *around, trying to lasso him, but they can't catch him. They knock over furniture trying. When they are tired, they sit down and rest.)*

HARRY. What shall we try next?

TOM. I'm thinking, I'm thinking. This is harder than I thought.

(*A sign, carried across the stage, says "Eight hours later." HARRY and TOM are a mess. The house is in shambles, and GHOST is still exercising.*)

HARRY. This is ridiculous! I'm bushed!

TOM. Me, too. Nothing has worked. We've tried everything I can think of. We've tried smoking him out. (HARRY *fans the air.*) We've tried hosing him out. (HARRY *wrings out a wet cloth.*) We've tried luring him out with candy bars. We've even tried skunk juice.

HARRY (*plugs his nose*). Yeah, and how are we ever going to get that smell out?

TOM. I don't know. This place is a mess. Mrs. Beazley's gonna kill us.

HARRY. Well, I guess we'll just have to clean it up the best we can. Then we can call and tell her we failed.

TOM. Okay, but first let's take a little break. I'm tired. I think I'll sit down, relax, and play this guitar for a while. I'm sure Mrs. Beazley won't mind.

HARRY. That'll be the least of her problems.

(*They both sit. GHOST sits, too, and begins reading a newspaper. TOM plays the guitar. He and HARRY start singing the song "Clementine." They are very off-key, but they think they sound great.*)

TOM & HARRY. Oh, my darling . . .

(GHOST *puts down the newspaper and covers his ears with his hands.*)

Oh, my darling . . .

(GHOST *shakes his head and tries harder to cover his ears and ignore them. He tries putting his newspaper over his head.*)

Oh, my darling Clementine . . .

(GHOST *gets up and starts pacing the room. He tries humming to drown out their singing.*)

You are lost and gone forever . . .

(GHOST *picks up two couch pillows and covers his ears. He puts his head under the cushions of the couch.*)

Dreadful sorry, Clementine!

GHOST (*throwing down the couch pillows*). I can't stand it anymore! You win!

(*He grabs a suitcase and starts packing, throwing in sheets and pillowcases, and any other "ghostlike" necessities.*)

I'm leaving!

(*He runs offstage.* TOM *and* HARRY *watch him, shrug their shoulders, and continue singing as the curtain closes.*)

THE END

THE FORGETFUL WITCH

Characters

MOTHER WITCH
BRUNHILDA (her daughter)
KITTEN
DOG
BIRD
BASEBALL PLAYER
STORE CLERK

Setting the Stage

For the witch costumes all you need are ordinary clothes plus hats and capes. For KITTEN and DOG you need only ears and tails, something simple so that they can be recognized. BIRD could use wings and a beak. BASEBALL PLAYER might wear a cap and carry a baseball bat. Optional set: A kitchen setup and a store setup at the back of the stage. Optional props: a cauldron and spoon for MOTHER WITCH to stir her potion, and some bottles and cans for ingredients.

SCENE. MOTHER WITCH *is stirring her potion. She adds a few ingredients, then looks for another.*

MOTHER WITCH. Oh, bother! I'm out of canned bats' wings. I can't finish my brew now. I know! I'll send Brunhilda to get some. Brunhilda! (*She calls.*) Come here, please!

(BRUNHILDA *enters.*)

BRUNHILDA. Yes, mother?

MOTHER WITCH. I'm all out of canned bats' wings. I need you to go to the store to get some for me.

BRUNHILDA. Okay, mother. Is that all you need?

MOTHER WITCH. Yes, just bats. You know how forgetful you can be, so don't forget—just bats.

BRUNHILDA. I won't forget. (*She begins walking to the store.*) Let's see now. I'll just keep saying bats over and over so I won't forget. Bats, bats, bats.

(*She continues walking.* KITTEN *enters, meowing.* BRUNHILDA *stops to play with it.*)

Hi, kitty. I'd love to stop and play, but I have to go to the store. I have to buy my mother some—um— what was it now? (KITTEN *meows.*) I know! It was milk! Milk, milk, milk.

(KITTEN *exits.* BRUNHILDA *walks on.* DOG *enters barking.* BRUNHILDA *stops to pet it.*)

Hi, puppy. You're sure cute. Well, I can't stay. I have to go to the store to get—uh—I can't remember.

(*She watches as* DOG *barks and an idea strikes her.*)

I know, it was bones. Bones, bones, bones.

(DOG *exits.* BRUNHILDA *walks on.* BIRD *comes onstage, chirping.* BRUNHILDA *watches it fly around.*)

Oh, what a pretty bird! Now what was I supposed to get? (*She looks at* BIRD.) Let's see—it was birdseed. Birdseed, birdseed, birdseed.

(BIRD *flies off*.)

Well, I'm almost to the store now, and my mom will be really happy to see I didn't forget what to buy. There's the store.

(BASEBALL PLAYER enters.)

BASEBALL PLAYER. Hi.

BRUNHILDA. Hello. Where are you going?

BASEBALL PLAYER. I have to go to practice. Where are you going?

BRUNHILDA. I have to go to the store.

BASEBALL PLAYER. Well, I have to go now. Bye.

BRUNHILDA. Bye. (*She watches* BASEBALL PLAYER *swing his bat*.) Now let's see. What was I supposed to get? I know—BATS!

(*She enters the store, buys the bats' wings from the clerk and runs home.* BASEBALL PLAYER *exits*.)

Mother, I'm home!

MOTHER WITCH. Oh, good. Did you remember to get bats?

BRUNHILDA. Yes, here they are.

MOTHER WITCH (*surprised*). Good job! I guess you aren't as forgetful as I thought you were.

BRUNHILDA. Of course not. I remember everything!

(*The curtain closes*.)

THE END

VAMPIRE SNACK

Blackout Sketch

Characters

TWO VAMPIRES

> **Note:** *This sketch can be used for any occasion, not just Halloween.*

SCENE. *One vampire, standing onstage, takes a can marked "blood," pours tomato juice from it into a glass and drinks it. The second vampire enters.*

VAMPIRE #1. Mmm. Delicious. Vould you like some?

VAMPIRE #2. No, thanks. I couldn't drink another bite.

VAMPIRE #1. So vat's new?

VAMPIRE #2. Nothing much. I just saw a poor old bum begging on the street corner.

VAMPIRE #1. You did. Vat did he say?

VAMPIRE #2. He vanted me to help him. He said he hadn't had a bite in days.

VAMPIRE #1. So vat did you do?

VAMPIRE #2. Vat else? Naturally, I bit him!

BLACKOUT

TRICK OR TREAT

Characters
MOTHER
CHILD

Setting the Stage
CHILD needs some kind of Halloween costume, plus an assortment of trick-or-treat candy.

SCENE. *A living room.* CHILD *is just returning home from trick-or-treating.*

CHILD. Hi, Mom, I'm home.

MOTHER. Oh, good. Did you have fun?

CHILD. Yeah, it was great. (*Holds out his bag to show* MOTHER.) I got a lot of candy.

MOTHER. Well, you know I have to check through your candy to make sure it's safe.

CHILD. Aw, Mom. I only went to houses where we knew the people. I didn't get *any* from strangers.

MOTHER. Well, you can never be too careful.

(*She begins looking through the bag. She starts putting the candy into a pile.*)

CHILD. What are you doing?

MOTHER. Well, I think I saw needle marks in all this candy. It might have poison or drugs in it. (*She puts an apple in the pile.*) And this probably has razor blades in it. (*Ripping the wrapper off a candy bar*) And this candy bar is partly open! Well, none of this is safe.

CHILD. Come on, Mom!

MOTHER. Besides, even if it is safe, it's terrible for your teeth. You'll get cavities, pimples, and just plain fat if you eat all this.

CHILD (*reaches into the bag and pulls out one candy bar*). This is all that's left!

MOTHER. That doesn't look safe, either. (*She begins to grab it.*)

CHILD (*pulling it away*). But Mom, I got this one from *our* house!

MOTHER. Oh, well, I guess you can have that one. Now go to bed. It's late and you have school tomorrow.

CHILD (*sadly*). Okay. Goodnight. (*Exit.*)

MOTHER (*to audience*). You never can be too sure about Halloween candy these days.

(*She opens some and begins to eat it.*)

The things a mother does to protect her children. But I have to check it to make sure it's okay, don't I?

(*She eats some more.*)

I just love Halloween!

(*The curtain closes.*)

THE END

GEE, THANKS

Blackout Sketch

Characters

BIFF
SALLY

SCENE. SALLY *is onstage.* BIFF *enters.*

BIFF. Hello, Sally, baby. Today is your lucky day!

SALLY. It is? Why?

BIFF. Because I decided to talk to you!

SALLY. Gee, thanks.

BIFF. Well, Sally, did you have a nice Thanksgiving?

SALLY. Yes, I did.

BIFF. I wanted to come over for dinner, but I couldn't. A super guy like me is in heavy demand, you know.

SALLY. Oh, I bet.

BIFF. We really have a lot to be thankful for, don't we?

SALLY. We sure do.

BIFF. (*putting his arm around* SALLY). Tell me, Sally, what were you most thankful for this year?

SALLY (*removing his arm*). Most thankful? I guess I was most thankful you didn't come for dinner!

BLACKOUT

THE FIRST THANKSGIVING

Characters
PILGRIM MEN AND WOMEN
INDIAN MEN AND WOMEN

Setting the Stage
Pilgrims wear hats and collars made of construction paper. Indians wear headbands and feathers. Setup for the feast is needed, including "turkey" (can be made from construction paper), pies and vegetables. Other props: Sign reading "Later That Day."

SCENE. THE PILGRIMS *are onstage, busily getting ready for the big feast.*

PILGRIM MAN #1. Well, we're just about ready for our big feast to begin. We've had a bountiful harvest and now it's time to give thanks.

PILGRIM MAN #2. Yes, and I'm glad we invited the Indians. They're the ones who helped us and taught us how to live in this new land.

(*Enter* INDIANS.)

PILGRIM WOMAN #1. Here they are now. Hello, friends, come join us.

INDIAN MAN #1. How.

INDIAN WOMAN #1. We ready for big feast. Bring pumpkin pie for dessert.

PILGRIM WOMAN #2. Pumpkin pie? What's that? It sounds awful.

INDIAN WOMAN #2. We would bring other kind of pie, but bananas not grow in this land. Pumpkin all we could find.

PILGRIM WOMAN #2. Uh, well, thanks for trying.

(She looks at friends and makes a face pointing at pie.)

PILGRIM WOMAN #1. But why did you bring dessert, anyway? We distinctly told you that you were in charge of bringing the roast beef.

INDIAN WOMAN #2. No, invitation say bring dessert.

PILGRIM WOMAN #3. No, no, no! You were supposed to bring roast beef!

(They start to argue.)

PILGRIM MAN #1. Let's not argue. We're here to celebrate. But now, the problem is, what do we eat? We have pumpkin pie and vegetables, but no meat. It won't be much of a feast.

PILGRIM MAN #2. We'll just have to go hunting and see what we can find to eat.

(A sign, carried across the stage, reads "Later That Day." When the curtain reopens, the PILGRIMS and INDIANS are sitting around waiting for the hunters to return. PILGRIM MAN #1 and INDIAN MAN #1 enter carrying a dead turkey.)

The First Thanksgiving ☆ 87

PILGRIM WOMAN #1. What on earth is that thing?

PILGRIM MAN #1. It's all we could find. It's some kind of bird. We'll just have to cook it and eat it for our feast.

INDIAN MAN #1. Bird called wild turkey.

PILGRIM WOMAN #3. Some feast! Pumpkin pie and turkey! Next year I want to be in charge of the organizing committee so that we can have a real feast!

PILGRIM MAN #1. Okay, okay, next year you're in charge, but in the meantime, please go and cook this thing.

(*The sign is carried across the stage again.* PILGRIM MEN *and all* INDIANS *are sleeping.* PILGRIM WOMEN *enter, carrying food.*)

PILGRIM WOMAN #1. Wake up! It's time to eat.

(*They all sit and start to eat.*)

PILGRIM MAN #2. Hey, this turkey is good!

INDIAN MAN #1. And how!

PILGRIM WOMAN #2. Say, this pumpkin pie is tasty, too. Maybe we should have this kind of feast every year. We could start a tradition.

PILGRIM WOMAN #3. Naw, it'll never catch on. This is good, but nothing will ever replace good old roast beef!

(*They continue to eat as curtain closes.*)

THE END

THANKSGIVING PIE CONTEST

Characters

DON
RUTH
THREE JUDGES
CONTESTANTS (as many as desired)

> **Note:** *This skit can easily be used for any occasion by changing the pumpkin pie to cherry, lemon, or some other dessert.*

Setting the Stage

Contestants could wear chef hats and full-length aprons with numbers pinned onto them. Judges should wear some distinguishing piece of clothing, such as a hat or sash. Tables are set up onstage where contestants "work." They are filled with cooking utensils and supplies. RUTH and DON's table is center stage. Foil pie plates are needed for the finished products. Other props: Pumpkin, egg, other ingredients; sign reading "Later."

SCENE. *The annual pie-baking contest.*

HEAD JUDGE. Welcome to our annual Thanksgiving pie-baking contest. Good luck to all you contestants. Now, let's begin!

DON. Are you ready?

RUTH. Of course. Now remember, you're here to help. Just let me do all the important stuff.

DON. Okay, I'll read the recipe to you. By the way, what are we making?

RUTH. It's a very special pumpkin-deluxe pie. Okay, now start reading the recipe to me.

DON. Three cups milk, two cups flour.

(RUTH *puts in the ingredients.*)

Oops! I read it wrong. It was supposed to be one-third cup milk, not three!

RUTH. Oh, dear. Oh, well, it won't make that much difference. Milk is good for you anyway.

DON. Now, let's see—one egg.

(RUTH *throws it in whole.* DON *doesn't notice. He is measuring the sugar.*)

DON. Here's two cups of sugar. I already measured it.

(RUTH *dumps in the sugar.*)

RUTH. Did you get the sugar from this bag? (*She holds up a bag.*)

DON. Yes, why?

RUTH. This isn't sugar, you idiot, it's salt!

DON. We'll just have to start all over.

RUTH. We can't. We don't have enough time. We'll just

have to hope it tastes okay. Now, what's next in the recipe?

DON. One pumpkin.

(*He holds it up and starts to put it into the bowl.*)

RUTH. Don't you think we should cut it up first?

DON. Uh—I guess so. (*He cuts it up and puts it in. He doesn't actually have to cut it. He can just pretend to and have something else to dump into the bowl.*)

RUTH. I think maybe we were supposed to take out the seeds first.

DON. Oh, well, they'll taste good with all that salt. (*He studies the recipe.*) Now just add a cup of marshmallows and a cup of chocolate chips, and we're all done.

RUTH. That's not in the recipe!

DON. It's my own special touch. Trust me, it'll be great. (*He stirs it.*) It looks kind of weird.

RUTH. Oh, well, it's too late to change it now. Just put it in the oven to bake.

(*The curtain closes. A sign, carried across the stage, reads "Later." The curtain opens. CONTESTANTS are lined up with their masterpieces on tables in front of them. RUTH and DON are at the end of the line. JUDGES are busily tasting and marking down scores on cards.*)

HEAD JUDGE (*tasting an entry*). Marvelous, very tasty.

JUDGE #2 (*tasting a different one*). Mmm—simply delicious!

(JUDGES *continue tasting and commenting on each entry. They finally come to* RUTH's *and* DON's *pie.*)

JUDGE #3 (*tasting it*). I've never tasted anything so wonderful.

JUDGE #2. I love it!

(JUDGES *get together to confer. They come back and put a ribbon on* RUTH *and* DON's *entry.*)

HEAD JUDGE. This entry wins by a mile. Now I simply must have the recipe.

RUTH. Well, okay. (*She starts to hand it over, but then holds back.*) Wait, I have to change a few things.

(RUTH *writes down the changes and hands the recipe to the judges. They being reading, look sick, hold their stomachs, and stagger offstage.*)

RUTH. What's wrong with them?

DON. I don't know. I guess they were overwhelmed because they liked our recipe so much.

(*They shake hands.* RUTH *picks up the pie and they exit happily as the curtain closes.*)

THE END

THE TICKET LINE

Blackout Sketch

Characters

FANS
MAN

SCENE. FANS *are standing in line waiting to buy tickets for "the big game."* MAN *enters at the end of the line.*

FAN #1. I can't wait to buy tickets!

FAN #2. Me neither. This is going to be the game of the year.

FAN #3. When are they going to open up? It seems like I've been waiting forever?

FAN #4. I don't know. I hope it'll be soon. I can't wait to get those tickets. This is going to be my best Thanksgiving ever—going to the big game.!

(As FANS are talking, MAN walks up to the front of the line.)

FAN #1. Hey, buddy, get to the end of the line!

(He pushes MAN back to the end and FANS continue to talk about the big game. As they are talking, MAN works his way back to the front of the line.)

FAN #1. Hey, you! I thought I told you to get back there at the end of the line!

(Again he shoves MAN back.)

FAN #2 (watching MAN being pushed back). The nerve of some people! (Looking at watch) I wonder what's taking them so long to open up?

(One last time, MAN pushes his way to the front of the line.)

FAN #1 (sees him). What's the matter with you? I'm first! I've been here all morning waiting to get the best seats for the big game. What makes you think a jerk like you can get ahead of me?

MAN (giving up). I quit! They'll just have to find someone else to open up this ticket booth!

BLACKOUT

GRANDMA'S HOUSE

Characters

MOTHER
SON
DAUGHTER
FATHER

Setting the Stage

SON and DAUGHTER can wear everyday clothing, but need bathrobes for the dream scene. MOTHER and FATHER may wish to wear "grown-up" clothes (high heels, long dress for MOTHER, suit and tie for FATHER). Parents also need bathrobes or some other grubby clothes for the dream scene. One side of the stage is set with living room furniture and television set, the other side with table and chairs. Special props: A mound of black construction paper can be used for the turkey in the dream scene; signs reading "Thanksgiving Without Grandma," "Later," and "Back to Reality."

SCENE. *Living room. The family is at home getting ready to go to Grandma's house for Thanksgiving.*

MOTHER. Come on, you guys. Let's get ready to go to Grandma's house.

SON. Do we have to go? I don't want to.

DAUGHTER. Yes, it's boring there. There's nothing to do. I'd rather stay home.

FATHER. Now, come on, kids. Grandma goes to a lot of trouble every Thanksgiving. You should be thankful instead of complaining.

MOTHER. Just imagine what Thanksgiving would be like without Grandma!

(They all freeze as the curtain closes. A sign, carried across the stage, reads, "Thanksgiving Without Grandma." The curtain opens to the family sitting around in bathrobes.)

FATHER *(looking around lazily and stretching)*. What day is it today?

SON. Don't you remember? It's Thanksgiving! That's why you stayed home from work.

FATHER. Oh, right. It doesn't seem like Thanksgiving without Grandma.

MOTHER. Oh, my goodness, I almost forgot! I have to cook a turkey today!

(MOTHER rushes off to the kitchen.)

SON. Does Mom know how to cook a turkey?

DAUGHTER. I guess so. She's never done it before. Grandma always did all the cooking for Thanksgiving.

SON. Well, I suppose we'll find out soon enough.

DAUGHTER. Turn on the television. I want to watch soap operas.

SON. Soap operas? Forget it!

DAUGHTER. We always watch soap operas at Grandma's house.

SON. But that's because Grandma has two television sets. We only have one and we're watching football.

DAUGHTER. No way! Over my dead body!

SON. Gladly!

(*They both run to the television set, wrestling over it. The knob comes off in* SON*'s hand.*)

DAUGHTER. Now look what you did!

SON. I did! You were the one pulling on my arm! You did it!

FATHER. Stop fighting, you two! (*He fusses with set.*) Well, that solves this argument. Nobody's watching anything because the television set is broken!

SON. Oh, brother! Now what are we going to do? It's all your fault!

DAUGHTER. No, sir, it's your fault!

(*They start wrestling again as* MOTHER *enters. She's a mess—her clothes disheveled, her hair all ratted up.*)

MOTHER. Stop it! I'm having enough trouble making this dinner without you two fighting. You sit over there. (*She sends* DAUGHTER *to one side of the room.*) And you over there. (SON *goes to the other side.*) Now stay there!

DAUGHTER. Okay, Mom.

(MOTHER *exits.*)

SON. Are we having fun yet?

(*The curtain closes. A sign reading "Later" is carried across the stage. When the curtain reopens,* SON, DAUGHTER, *and* FATHER *are in the same positions.* FATHER *is sleeping; the others look very bored.*)

DAUGHTER. This is so boring!

SON. Oh, well, it should be time to eat soon.

DAUGHTER. Isn't anyone else coming over? Grandma always has lots of company for Thanksgiving dinner.

SON. Are you kidding? Mom wouldn't invite anyone over because she's never cooked Thanksgiving dinner before. Hey, what's that smell?

DAUGHTER. I guess it's dinner. Doesn't smell quite like Grandma's house, does it?

(MOTHER *enters.*)

MOTHER. Time for dinner, I guess.

FATHER (*wakes up*). Dinner? Great! I'm starved.

(*They sit at the table.* MOTHER *exits, returns carrying*

a large platter with a crumpled-up burnt thing on it.)

SON. What's that?

MOTHER (*begins to cry*). It's the turkey!

FATHER. It's okay. It'll probably taste—uh (*he looks doubtful*)—delicious. (*He stands to lead the prayer.*) Let's say the prayer now in honor of our—uh— lovely Thanksgiving.

(*The curtain closes. A sign carried across the stage reads, "Back to Reality." The curtain reopens with the family in their good clothes.*)

SON. Everyone get your coats. Hurry! We'll be late to Grandma's!

DAUGHTER. Yeah, let's go!

MOTHER. But I thought. . . .

SON. Never mind. There's no place I'd rather be on Thanksgiving than Grandma's house. Now let's get moving!

EVERYONE. Okay, let's go!

(*They follow* SON *offstage as the curtain closes.*)

THE END

TURKEY CONTEST

Characters
SEVERAL TURKEYS
THREE JUDGES

Setting the Stage

Turkeys could wear brown clothes and "feathers" made from construction paper. They have large numbers pinned to their fronts. JUDGES could all wear hats or other identifying clothing. TURKEY #1 needs rags or pillows for "stuffing."

SCENE. *The annual turkey contest. The turkeys are standing around waiting to be judged.*

TURKEY #1 (*looking around at other contestants*). Boy, do I have it made! Look at the competition around here. I can't lose!

TURKEY #2. Oh, I don't know. There are some pretty fine-looking turkeys here. I think that one is plumper than you are. (*Points to another turkey.*)

TURKEY #1. Plump? It's just plain fat! How could that win?

TURKEY #3. Turkeys are judged by their measurements, you know. The plumper you are, the better chance you have of winning.

TURKEY #1. Really? Well, I'll have to do something about that. (*Exits.*)

TURKEY #3 (*watches him exit*). Where's he going?

TURKEY #4. Who knows? But if he doesn't hurry, he'll miss the contest. It's about to start!

HEAD JUDGE. Ladies and gentlemen, welcome to the annual turkey contest. Are the contestants ready to begin?

(*The turkeys nod and begin forming a line.* TURKEY #1 *runs in, rags and pillows stuffed under his clothes.*)

TURKEY #1. Hey, wait for me!

(*He pushes his way into line, unaware that rags are hanging out underneath his "feathers."*)

TURKEY #2. What's this?

(*He pulls at the "stuffing" in* TURKEY #1.)

A little "stuffing," eh?

TURKEY #1 (*pushing the "stuffing" back inside*). Mind your own business!

TURKEY #4. He really wants to win, doesn't he?

TURKEY #3. I guess so.

HEAD JUDGE. All right, the judging will now begin.

(JUDGES *get out measuring tape and check turkey measurements. Then* JUDGES *get in a circle and decide on the winner.*)

HEAD JUDGE. The choice of the judges is unanimous. Because of his measurements the winner of the annual turkey contest is Turkey #1!

(*The other turkeys huddle around* TURKEY #1, *congratulating him.*)

TURKEY #1. Of course, I was the obvious choice. But hey! Where are my prizes?

JUDGES. Prizes?

TURKEY #1. Yeah, you know, a new car, $1,000, a trip to Hawaii, or something like that?

HEAD JUDGE. I'm afraid you don't understand. *You* are the prize.

TURKEY #1. I don't get it.

HEAD JUDGE. The winner of the Turkey Contest doesn't *get* any prizes. He *becomes* the prize. He gets to be Thanksgiving Dinner!

TURKEY #1. Dinner, who, me? Oh, no, you don't!

(*He begins running around,* JUDGES *chasing him.*)

HEAD JUDGE (*stops and speaks to audience*). I just love to see a happy winner! Well, time to go! Happy Thanksgiving!

(*He continues chasing as the curtain closes.*)

THE END

Skits & Sketches for Any Time

HICCUP FOR ME

Characters
SAM
LINDA
REX
MELISSA
DALE
TEX
MRS. BELL (teacher)

Setting the Stage
No props or special costumes are necessary.

SCENE. *Study hall in school.* MRS. BELL *is at her desk, correcting papers. All students are onstage, supposedly studying.*

SAM. Hic—oh, boy! I'm never going to—hic—get rid of these darn hic—hiccups! I've tried—hic—everything I can think of.

(*He looks disgusted as* LINDA *and* REX *come up to his desk.*)

LINDA. Hi, ya, Sam. What's the matter?

SAM. I've got the hic—hiccups!

LINDA. I'll be right back. (LINDA *goes offstage.*)

REX. I've got a great way to get rid of hiccups. It always works.

(LINDA *returns, wearing a monster mask.* SAM *doesn't see her.*)

SAM (*to* REX). What is it? I'll try anything.

LINDA (*creeping up on* SAM). BOO!

SAM. What was that—hic—for?

LINDA. To scare your hiccups away. It works every time.

SAM. Well, it didn't—hic—work this time.

REX. Try my system. Hold your breath for one minute. That'll do it. I'll time you.

SAM. Hic—okay. (*He holds his breath.*)

REX (*timing him, speaking to* LINDA). It works every time. I've had the hiccups millions of times and I always hold my breath and then they go away. I'm really not sure why it works, but it does. . . .

(*He goes on talking, forgetting about* SAM, *who is still holding his breath and by this time about to die.* SAM *waves his arms frantically.*)

LINDA (*interrupts*). Uh-oh, we forgot about Sam!

REX. Oh, yeah, you can breath now. It's been more than a minute.

SAM. Man, I thought I was going to die!

LINDA. Did it work?

SAM. Uh, yeah, I guess.

REX. See? I told you. It works every time!

(REX *goes back to his seat.*)

SAM. I'm so happy to get rid of those hic—hiccups. Oh, no! They're hic—back! Now what do I hic—do?

(MELISSA *approaches* SAM's *desk.*)

LINDA. Hey, do you know how to get rid of hiccups?

MELISSA. Sure! The best way I know is to sing the ABC Song. It gets your mind off the hiccups long enough so that they just go away.

SAM. Are you sure that'll—hic—work?

MELISSA. Sure, it works every time!

SAM. Okay. (*He sings.*) A, B, C—hic—D, E, F—hic—G, H, I, J, K, L, M, N, O—hic—P, Q, R—hic—S, T, U, V, W, X, Y, Z. Hey, I think it did work! Thanks!

MELISSA. No problem, it works every time.

(MELISSA *goes back to her desk.* DALE *and* TEX *approach* SAM's *desk.*)

SAM. I'll have to remember that one. Sing the—hic—ABC's. Oh, no! They didn't go—hic—away!

DALE. You got the hiccups? (SAM *nods.*) Try jumping up and down backwards on one leg. It works every time.

(SAM *begins hopping.*)

TEX. No, I have a better one. Plug your nose and wave your other arm up and down like a bird. That really works.

(*Still hopping,* SAM *plugs his nose and waves his arm.*)

DALE. You'll see. It'll work.

(DALE *and* TEX *sit back down to study.*)

LINDA. Is it working?

SAM. I don't know. (*He stops.*) But I feel—hic—ridiculous! Everybody says it'll—hic—work every time, but nothing does for—hic—me!

(MRS. BELL *looks up from her work.*)

LINDA. The teacher's looking at you. Why don't we ask her if you can get a drink of water? Maybe that'll help.

SAM. Hic—okay.

LINDA. Mrs. Bell, can Sam go get a drink of water? He has the hiccups.

MRS. BELL (*to* SAM). Okay, but first hiccup for me.

SAM. What?

MRS. BELL. Hiccup for me, so I'll know you're telling the truth.

SAM (*tries but after a long pause*). I can't hiccup—they're all gone! I mean it! They're really gone. I can't hiccup for you! Hooray! I feel so much better! My hiccups are really gone!

MRS. BELL. I know. It works every time.

(MRS. BELL *exits.* SAM *shrugs his shoulders. Just as the curtain is closing, he hiccups again and falls to the floor in despair.*)

THE END

MIXED-UP MAGIC

Characters

CARLI
TERRY
MOTHER

Setting the Stage

CARLI needs no special costume. MOTHER may wish to wear a longer dress, high heels, apron and such. Toys and clothes, books, tapes, etc. are needed to "mess up" CARLI's room. Other props: Sign reading, "Hours Later."

SCENE. CARLI's *room is a mess.* CARLI *and* TERRY *are playing, when* CARLI's MOTHER *enters.*

MOTHER. Carli, this room is a mess! You need to clean it up.

CARLI. Okay, Mom, as soon as we're done playing.

MOTHER. I'm going shopping now, and I want it clean by the time I get back. When you're finished cleaning, you may go outside and play, but not before.

(*She exists.* CARLI *begins searching the room.*)

TERRY. Don't you hate cleaning your room?

CARLI. I always have before, but today I have a solution. Now where is that book of magic spells?

TERRY. Magic spells? You can't be serious!

CARLI. Oh, yes, I am—just watch me. I'm going to use magic to clean up this mess. Only—I can't find my book. Oh, there it is!

(*She picks up the book and begins searching for the right spell.*)

I know it's in here somewhere. I just can't find it. I guess I'll just have to play it by ear!

TERRY. Do you think you can?

CARLI. No problem. This is one of the easiest spells. I read it in here before. I practically have it memorized. Let's see—what were those magic words? Hmm, Abra-cadabra—clean my room! That oughta do it.

(*She raises her arms and waves them around. A pile of toys and clothes come flying in from off stage.*)

CARLI. Uh-oh—I guess I goofed a little.

TERRY. That was amazing! How did you do that?

CARLI. Well, it wasn't exactly the result I was after. I'll just have to try again. Let's see—Hocus-pocus—clean my room!

(*Again she raises her arms and waves them. Again a pile of toys and clothes comes flying in from off stage.*)

Oh, no! I got it backwards again? This is getting to be a real mess! Maybe I should give up. But I was sure I knew that spell. I'll just give it one more try and then if it doesn't work, I'll have to give up. Alacazam!—clean my room!

(*Again more toys and clothes are tossed in from offstage.*)

TERRY. This is the messiest room I've ever seen!

CARLI. We'll just have to clean it by hand. It'll probably take us hours!

TERRY. Us? Gosh, I forgot, I have to go home now. Bye!

(*She rushes offstage.* CARLI *begins picking up toys as the curtain closes. A sign carried across the stage reads, "Hours Later." The curtain reopens.* CARLI *is picking up the last few items.*)

CARLI. I'm just about done. Thank goodness. I'm so tired. I never want to see another mess like that as long as I live!

(*She picks up the magic book and walks over to dump it in the wastebasket.*)

I've had enough of this hocus-pocus. Good-bye and good riddance!

(*As she drops it into the basket, more clothes and toys come flying offstage.*)

Oh, no! Not again!

(*She faints as the curtain closes.*)

THE END

DOGGIE DOCTOR

Blackout Sketch

Characters

MAN

PSYCHIATRIST

Setting the Stage

MAN needs no special costume. PSYCHIATRIST could wear a white coat and glasses. He has a desk and also a couch on one side of the stage.

SCENE. PSYCHIATRIST's *office.* PSYCHIATRIST *is doing paperwork at his desk.* MAN *enters on his hands and knees. He sniffs around the room a bit. He scratches the back of his head a few times with his foot as if he has fleas. Then he starts barking.* PSYCHIATRIST *stares at him, stands, and goes over to him.*

PSYCHIATRIST. May I help you, sir?

MAN (*howls like a dog*).

PSYCHIATRIST. This is ridiculous. I'm much too busy to waste my time. Either tell me why you're here, sir, or I'll have my secretary show you out.

MAN. Oh, uh, I'm sorry, doc. That's why I'm here. You see, I have this problem.

PSYCHIATRIST. What's the problem?

MAN. Well, you see, doctor, my problem is that I think I'm a dog.

(*He holds up his arms like paws and pants like a dog.*)

PSYCHIATRIST. Hmm. How long have you had this problem?

MAN. Oh, ever since I was a puppy!

PSYCHIATRIST. Well, lie down on the couch and we'll talk about it.

MAN. Oh, no, I can't.

PSYCHIATRIST. Why not?

MAN. I'm not allowed on the furniture!

PSYCHIATRIST. I see. Well, I believe I can help you.

MAN. Yes, doctor. What's your advice for me?

PSYCHIATRIST. Be sure to get your shots and don't go chasing any cars!

(PSYCHIATRIST *exits.*)

BLACKOUT

THE SINGER

Blackout Sketch

Characters

SINGER
FRIEND

> **Note:** *This sketch may be used in a talent show or revue after somebody sings a funny song.*

SCENE. *A stage.* SINGER *enters and prepares to entertain the audience.*

SINGER. Tonight, ladies and gentlemen, I shall entertain you with my gorgeous appearance and my incredible singing voice. I will start with one of my all-time favorites.

(SINGER *performs a song in a terrible, off-key voice that gets louder as it goes along.* SINGER *dances, too—badly—oblivious to the fact that the performance is awful. At the end,* FRIEND *enters.*)

SINGER (*to* FRIEND). The audience isn't clapping. They must be so overwhelmed—so moved—so stunned—by my performance that they can't react.

FRIEND. Well, you might say that.

SINGER. I'll just have to sing another of my favorites. Let's see, what should I sing?

FRIEND. No, no—I think you'd better quit now.

SINGER. But why?

FRIEND. Poor health.

SINGER. But I'm in wonderful health. I'm strong. I've never felt better. What do you mean I should quit because of poor health?

FRIEND. Not *your* poor health. (*Pointing to the audience*) You're making those other people sick!

BLACKOUT

FRIENDS OF YOURS?

Blackout Sketch

Characters
GOMER
GOPHER
GOOBER
POLICEMAN

SCENE. *The park.* GOMER, GOPHER *and* GOOBER *are sitting on a park bench.* GOOBER *is quietly reading.* GOMER *is pretending to be swimming in a lake. He stands on the bench, jumps off and "swims" around.* GOPHER *is pretending to be fishing. He casts off, waits, and then reels in fish after fish.* POLICEMAN *enters and watches them.)*

GOMER. Watch this dive!

(*He pretends to dive and swim around.*)

GOPHER. That was a 7.5. You didn't point your toes enough. Now, here it goes again. (*He pretends to cast off.*) Yahoo, another big one! I got another bite!

(*He pretends to fight with the fish as he reels it in.*)

Come on, now. Come to Papa. I got him! What a beauty!

(*He holds up his imaginary fish for the others to see.*)

GOMER. Wow, it looks like another twenty-pounder!

(*They continue their activities.*)

POLICEMAN (*to* GOOBER). Excuse me, sir, but do you know these two men?

GOOBER. Yes, Officer. I'm afraid they're my friends.

POLICEMAN. Well, sir, I think maybe you better get them out of here before somebody gets hurt.

GOOBER. No problem, Officer. Come on, you guys. Get back in the boat.

(*They all pretend to jump into a boat and* GOOBER *pretends to row the boat offstage.* POLICEMAN *shakes his head.*)

BLACKOUT

SPELLING CONTEST

Characters
AARON
CHERYL
ANNIE
JASON
TWO JUDGES

Setting the Stage
No special costumes are needed. Contestants should have numbers pinned to the fronts of their shirts, and judges should have badges to distinguish them from contestants. A list of spelling words, toy guns and a trophy are also needed.

SCENE. *Contestants stand in a line facing the audience. JUDGES stand at the side, presiding over the event. A trophy sits on a table at the other side of the stage.*

JUDGE #1. It's time for the annual spelling contest. Is everyone ready?

CONTESTANTS. Yes.

JUDGE #2. Good luck, then. Let's begin.

JUDGE #1. Contestant Number 1, step forward, please.

(AARON *steps forward.*)

Your word is "dictionary." I looked up a word in the dictionary.

AARON. Dictionary, D-I-C-T-I-O-N-E-R-Y, dictionary.

JUDGE #2 (*confers with* JUDGE #1). Sorry, that's wrong.

(*He gets out his gun and shoots* AARON. AARON *falls and dies. Everyone else carries on as if nothing has happened.*)

JUDGE #1. Contestant Number 2, step forward, please.

(CHERYL *steps forward.*)

Your word is "house." I live in a white house.

CHERYL. House, H-O-U-S-E, house.

JUDGE #2 (*confers with* JUDGE #1). You are right! Very good!

JUDGE #1. Contestant Number 3, step forward, please.

(ANNIE *steps forward.*)

Your word is "mayonnaise." Please put mayonnaise on my burger.

ANNIE. Mayonnaise, M-A-Y-O-N-A-Z-E, mayonnaise.

JUDGE #2 (*confers with* JUDGE #1). Sorry, that's wrong.

(He gets out his gun and shoots her. She falls to the ground, dead.)

JUDGE #1. Contestant Number 4, step forward, please.

(JASON steps forward.)

Your word is "mathematics." Please study mathematics.

JASON. Mathematics, M-A-T-H-E-M-A-T-I-C-S, mathematics.

JUDGE #2 *(confers with JUDGE #1)*. Sorry, that's wrong.

(He begins to point his gun at JASON.)

JASON. Wait! It was right! I'm sure I spelled it correctly. You guys need to check again!

(JUDGES again confer, checking their lists carefully.)

JUDGE #1. You were right.

JUDGE #2. *We* were wrong.

(They get out their guns and shoot each other at the same time. They fall to the ground, dead. JASON and CHERYL look at each other and shrug.)

JASON. I guess that means we both win. *(They pick up the trophy together and shake hands as the curtain closes.)*

THE END

THE PRISONER

Blackout Sketch

Characters
JUDGE
POLICEMAN
PRISONER

SCENE. *Courtroom.* JUDGE *is sitting at bench.* POLICEMAN *brings in* PRISONER, *stands before him.*

JUDGE. What's the charge?

POLICEMAN. We caught this man red-handed. He's a thief.

JUDGE (*to* PRISONER). Is this true?

PRISONER. Well, maybe so and maybe not.

JUDGE. Have you ever stolen anything?

PRISONER. Mmm . . . now and then.

JUDGE (*getting impatient*). Where did you steal things?

PRISONER. Oh, here and there.

JUDGE (*to* POLICEMAN). Lock this prisoner up!

(JUDGE *pounds his gavel.* POLICEMAN *begins to drag* PRISONER *away.*)

PRISONER. Wait—when do I get out of jail?

JUDGE (*smugly*). Oh, sooner or later!

BLACKOUT

MARTIAN MAMA

Blackout Sketch

Characters

MARTIAN MAMA
MARTIAN JUNIOR

Setting the Stage

The only essential part of the costume is an extra set
of arms pinned under Mama's regular arms. You can
make these arms from sleeves of old clothes stuffed
with newspaper.

> **Note:** *This sketch can be changed easily to suit any kind of alien or monster. Just change the names of the foods.*

SCENE. *MAMA is washing dishes, with her back turned to the audience. JUNIOR is sitting in a high chair eating dinner. The audience can't see Mama's extra arms because her back is turned.*

JUNIOR. Mama, I want something to drink! Gimme something to drink! (*He pounds his fists on his tray.*)

MAMA. I just did, Junior. It's right in front of you, dear.

JUNIOR (*picks up a glass of green-colored water.*) Gimme some moon-cheese pie, and more asteroid pudding, too. Come on, gimme it!

MAMA. Just a minute. Can't you see I'm busy with these dishes?

JUNIOR (*throws his water on the floor*). Uh-oh, Mama, my comet juice spilled. Hurry, clean it up! Mama, I want my dessert! Gimme my dessert!

MAMA (*turns around, revealing her four arms*). I can't do everything! I only have four arms!

BLACKOUT

THE TOOTHACHE

Characters

CHRIS
MATT
LAURIE
RYAN
LES

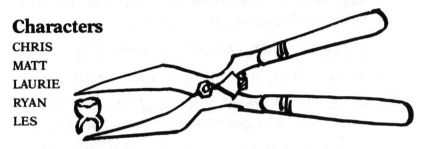

Setting the Stage

No special costumes are necessary. Props needed: a fake tooth, bag of apples, string, a door, pliers, and garden clippers; sign: "Later."

SCENE. CHRIS *is standing onstage, hands in his mouth, trying to wiggle his loose tooth.* MATT *enters.*

MATT. What's up, Chris?

CHRIS. Hi, Matt. My tooth is loose and I'm trying to get it out.

MATT. You say it's loose? Why don't you just try pulling it out?

CHRIS. I did, but it won't come out.

MATT. Say, I just happen to have some pliers here in my pocket. I'll pull it out for you.

CHRIS. You carry pliers around in your pocket? (MATT *nods.*) Well, okay, I guess.

(MATT *pulls out fake tooth with pliers.*)

Youch!

MATT. I got it, see? (*He holds up the tooth.*)

CHRIS. You got it, all right, but that was the wrong tooth! And now you're really gonna get it!

(*He chases* MATT *offstage, begins moaning.*)

Now my mouth hurts, and my tooth is still loose!

(*He alternately covers each side of his mouth with his hand.* LAURIE *enters carrying a bag of apples.*)

LAURIE. What's the matter, Chris?

CHRIS. My tooth is loose, and it won't come out. Matt pulled the wrong tooth out, and now the other side of my mouth hurts, too.

LAURIE. I just happen to have these apples here. Why don't you try biting one? That usually works for me. Here, take the whole bag.

CHRIS. Okay, that might work.

(*He exits with the apples. A sign carried across the stage reads, "Later." * CHRIS *returns carrying an apple. Now he holds his stomach and his mouth in pain.*)

LAURIE. Now what's wrong? Didn't biting a hard apple work?

CHRIS. No! (*He holds up the apple.*) I ate about twenty apples. My tooth is still loose, my mouth still hurts, and *now* I have a stomachache, too! Ow!

(*He continues yowling.* LAURIE *gives up and leaves.* RYAN *enters.*)

RYAN. What's the matter, Chris?

CHRIS (*snaps at him*). Everything! It's all because of this dumb loose tooth.

RYAN. Loose tooth? I know how to get it out. Just tie a string to your tooth, tie the other end to the door-knob, and then slam the door. Here—I just happen to have some string. Let's try it.

CHRIS. I don't know. (*He backs off a little.*)

RYAN. Come on, I'll do it for you. (*He pretends to tie string to tooth.*) Now, tell me when you're ready.

(*He gets behind the door and ties the other end.* CHRIS *mumbles something with the string in his mouth.* RYAN *opens the door with* CHRIS *right behind it. The doors slams into* CHRIS's *face.*)

RYAN. What did you say? Oops, sorry! (*He runs off-stage.*)

CHRIS. Now I have a headache (*rubs his head*), a stom-achache (*rubs his stomach*), my mouth still hurts (*rubs his jaw*), and my tooth is *still* loose. I'm a mess!

(*He groans and continues rubbing his head, stom-ach, and jaw.* LES *enters carrying garden clippers. As he enters, he is saying his line.*)

LES. Hey, Chris, I heard you have a toothache. Need some help? I just happen to have—

CHRIS (*sees clippers*). NO! NO WAY! NOT THAT!

(*He runs offstage. The curtain closes.*)

THE END

UP HAROLD

Characters

MAD SCIENTIST
HAROLD THE MONSTER
VOLUNTEER

Setting the Stage

MAD SCIENTIST needs a raincoat and glasses. HAROLD needs a monster mask and a table to lie on.

SCENE. HAROLD *is lying motionless on a table upstage.* MAD SCIENTIST *enters and speaks to the audience.*

MAD SCIENTIST. Hello, ladies and gentlemen. Today I'd like to demonstrate my newest invention. I call him Harold. He's really quite amazing. Watch, I'll show you what he can do. But before we start, I'll need a volunteer. Would anyone like to help out?

(*He pretends to search through the audience, but picks a predetermined volunteer.*)

You, sir, come up here, please. Stand right here.

(*He stations* VOLUNTEER *downstage, facing the audience.* VOLUNTEER*'s back is to* HAROLD.)

Are you ready, sir?

VOLUNTEER. Yes, I guess so. (*He shrugs his shoulders.*)

MAD SCIENTIST. Now, ladies and gentlemen, I will show you what this amazing creature can do. Watch this. Stand up, Harold.

(HAROLD *stands, his arms raised forward.*)

Walk forward, Harold.

(HAROLD *walks stiffly forward, toward the unsuspecting* VOLUNTEER. VOLUNTEER *looks a little bored.*)

Kill, Harold!

(HAROLD *grabs* VOLUNTEER *from behind and strangles him.* VOLUNTEER *struggles, fades and falls to the floor, dead.* HAROLD *stiffly returns to his table.*)

MAD SCIENTIST. Wasn't that great? I told you he was amazing. Now, who wants to be the next volunteer? I just love it—all I have to say is, "Stand up, Harold."

(MAD SCIENTIST *doesn't realize it, but* HAROLD *stands.*)

Then, after he stands up, all I have to say is, "Walk forward, Harold."

(HAROLD *sneaks up behind* MAD SCIENTIST.)

Then, it's really easy. I just say, "Kill, Harold."

(HAROLD *begins to strangle* MAD SCIENTIST *who tries to fight back.*)

Not me, you dummy!

(*They struggle and* MAD SCIENTIST *dies. The curtain closes as* HAROLD *begins to walk stiffly, arms raised towards the audience as if they are next.*)

THE END

INDEX